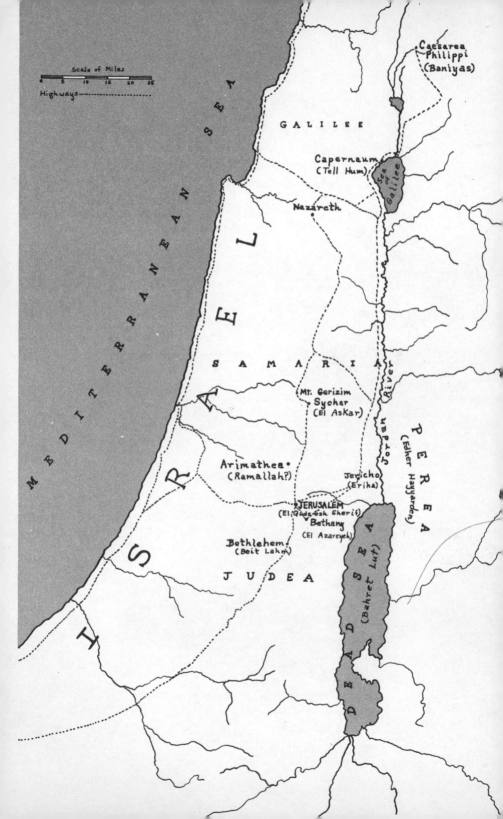

The Bold Galilean

The Bold Galilean

By George Holwager

The Bethany Press

St. Louis, Missouri

Contents

CHAPTER   PAGE

1. A Wonderful Trip _ _ _ _ _ _ _ _   11

2. The Great City _ _ _ _ _ _ _ _ _   23

3. From Boy to Man _ _ _ _ _ _ _ _   37

4. Night in the Wilderness _ _ _ _ _ _ _   45

5. Four Men and a Boat _ _ _ _ _ _ _   57

6. The Lion Begins to Roar _ _ _ _ _ _   71

7. The Sea and the Wind _ _ _ _ _ _ _   83

8. Light on the Mountain _ _ _ _ _ _ _   93

9. King for a Day _ _ _ _ _ _ _ _ _   107

10. When Everything Goes Wrong _ _ _ _ _   121

11. Sunrise Forever _ _ _ _ _ _ _ _ _   137

Before You Read This Book

THIS STORY OF THE LIFE OF JESUS has been written to give you a better understanding of him, and a greater appreciation of his significance for your life and the world in which you live.

It is not possible to write a story of the life of Jesus that tells what he did from day to day. The writers of the Gospels did not tell that kind of story. Some students of his life have estimated that the Gospels record events that took place in about 50 days of his life. If they are correct you can see how much more there was to tell than was recorded.

In this book, and particularly in the first three chapters, there is considerable material that is not drawn from the Gospels simply because they do not record details of that period of the life of Jesus. The writer has drawn upon his imagination to give us the story as it could have happened. And yet it is not pure imagination since it is based on what is known about life in the time of Jesus. The writer has tried always to give a picture of the personality, nature and character of Jesus as the Gospels present him.

As you read this book you will note frequent scripture references. This is done so you can turn to the Bible and read the story as it is given there.

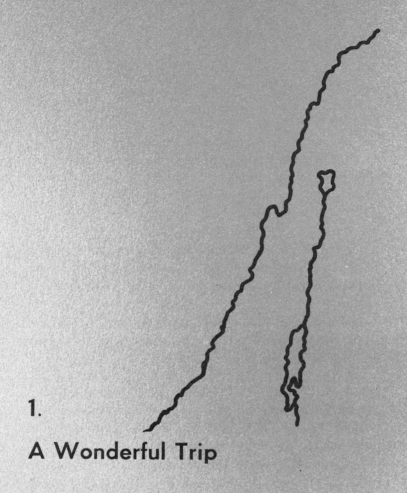

1.

A Wonderful Trip

THE BOY WAKENED with a start. Something had him by the feet and seemed to be dragging him away from the campfire beside which he had gone to sleep. The fire was nearly out and it was so dark he could not see what had hold of him. There flashed through his mind the stories of the wild animals the men had been telling as he fell off to sleep. His hair stood on end and he was about to scream for help when he heard a familiar voice.

"Jesus, Jesus," the voice said in a whisper.

"Have you forgotten?" It was Joseph shaking him by the ankle and reminding him of his duty.

Quickly now Jesus was awake. It was his first night in camp as fire tender. Now that he was 12 years old he had been given the man-sized job of keeping the fire going during the night. He hurried to the dying embers and blew them back to life, adding some twigs and then some larger pieces of wood. Jesus knew that if the fire had gone out it would have been difficult to start another. It was good to see the shooting flames.

He sat beside the fire awhile, watching to see if it would burn properly and as he did, he thought of all the thrilling things that had happened to him in the last few months.

The wonderful events had begun the week he became 12 years old. On the sabbath day (Saturday to us) he was presented in the synagogue (sin'a-gog) and became a member of it. For the first time he was allowed to sit on the men's side for the worship services. Up until this time he had gone with his mother and younger brothers and sisters to the women's side. It made him feel grown up to sit with the men.

After this he was no longer called *katon*, "little boy," by his parents and other adults. He was now called *gadol*, "grown-up person." This meant that he had left off being a child and was now becoming a man. It meant, too, that he would begin to do a man's work. Instead of helping his mother most of the time with the work about the house, he would help Joseph in the carpenter shop and on the little farm back of it.

Then came the birthday party when all the relatives had gathered for a feast and he was the honored guest. Cookies and raisins sweetened with honey were served to all the children present so that they would remember the event all their lives. Everybody had a happy time and

12

Jesus had been the happiest of them all. He smiled into the campfire as he remembered that glad day.

He thought of the long coat he had on. It had been a present from his mother and it was a very special coat. For one thing, it had been woven without a seam down the back such as most coats had. His mother had the largest loom in all Nazareth, made for her by the skillful hands of Joseph, and on it she could weave cloth wide enough to make a whole coat. The coat was long and of heavy wool and it served both as a coat on cool days and as a blanket when sleeping out of doors. Tonight for the first time he had used it as a blanket.

He felt of the leather moneybag Joseph had given him, now well filled with coins. His grandparents had given him several to start with and he had saved several more from his small earnings. These he would spend as he chose on this important trip.

But the most thrilling thing about these happy months had been the knowledge that he would make the trip with his parents to worship in the temple at Jerusalem. He had dreamed about it and saved for it and at last he was on his way. Early that morning a band of pilgrims had gathered at the synagogue in Nazareth and, led by the rabbi (rab'ī), they had set out on the road to Jerusalem. The trip would take three weeks, a week on the road each way and a week spent in the great city. They would camp out along the road each night and cook their meals over campfires. It was a thrilling journey for a boy of twelve.

The trip had seemed a long way off at the time of his birthday but the weeks had gone by swiftly, for there had been much to do in preparation for it. He had spent long hours at the synagogue school. The synagogue was used as a place of worship on the sabbath and as a school through the week. The rabbi served as both minister and schoolteacher. Here Jesus had begun to study the ancient

13

Hebrew language of his people. The Bible of that day, known as the Torah (tō'ra), contained only the part we call the Old Testament and was written in Hebrew. The words were hard to read and took much study. He was required to learn some passages from memory. One of these passages he had to learn in Hebrew was:

> The LORD said to Moses, "Speak to the people of Israel, and bid them to make tassels on the corners of their garments throughout their generations, and to put upon the tassel of each corner a cord of blue; and it shall be to you a tassel to look upon and remember all the commandments of the LORD, to do them, not to follow after your own heart and your own eyes, which you are inclined to go after wantonly. So you shall remember and do all my commandments, and be holy to your God. I am the LORD your God, who brought you out of the land of Egypt, to be your God: I am the LORD your God.
>
> --Numbers 15:37-41

There were three other 12-year-old boys in the school and the rabbi had told them that the one who learned the verses first would be chosen as a fire tender on the trip to Jerusalem. Boylike, Jesus had wanted that honor for himself and he had studied hard. Then came the day of the test. He had been called upon first and he did well at first but near the end he said the wrong Hebrew word and had to go back and correct himself. When he sat down, he was sure he had lost out.

Then the second boy had been called on to recite but he forgot near the middle and never did get all the way through. The third boy started out rapidly, reciting without a falter. Then near the end this boy got mixed up

14

and said several words wrong. Jesus knew he had won. His feelings were mixed. He was glad to have won, yet he thought how the other boys must feel. They had tried hard and failed. He had felt sorry with them. But suddenly he had an idea that would make them all happy.

"Why can't we all be fire tenders?" he had asked the rabbi. "So many people are going to Jerusalem this year that we will need more than one campfire."

"That is a good suggestion," the rabbi had answered with a smile. "We will see if that can be arranged."

But it had turned out that one of the boys could not go to Jerusalem. His father was very poor and could not afford to make the long and expensive trip. In the end it had been arranged that the two boys would keep two fires going in the camp each night.

It was necessary to keep the fires burning all night because there were no matches in those days and it would take a long time to get new fires started on which to cook breakfast for the pilgrims.

Now Jesus looked across the camp and saw another fire glowing brightly. The other boy was on his job and it made him feel good that he had a faithful helper. If ever either fire went out, it could be started again with coals from the other.

He went back to his sleeping place and rolled up in his long coat. But sleep did not come quickly, and he lay looking at the stars. They seemed almost close enough to touch. Silently he thanked God for their friendly light. Then he fell to thinking about the city of Jerusalem and the great temple there. He had studied about them in the synagogue school. What must they be like? He loved the town of Nazareth, but Jerusalem must be the most beautiful city in the world. He had been taught that it was God's holy city since the temple was there. What must that temple be like? He knew that in it there was

15

a dark, curtained-off place where God was supposed to dwell. Did he really live there or was he everywhere? He felt that God was very near to him tonight, as close as the stars felt close. Would it be different in the temple? Would God seem nearer than ever? Thinking about these things he fell off to sleep but not so soundly this time that he failed to wake up from time to time to put more wood on the fire.

Next morning the pilgrims were on their way again soon after sunup, and about noon they left the province of Galilee in which the town of Nazareth was located and entered the country of Samaria. Before crossing over into this country they stopped long enough to organize the group for protection in case any trouble arose, for it was a dangerous road ahead. Some of the younger men were chosen to march ahead of the group and keep a sharp lookout for any bands of Samaritans coming their way. Another group of men armed with heavy clubs were to stay behind and ward off any attack that might come from the rear. The rest, including the women, walked in a close group in the center with armed men scattered through the group.

All this was done because the Samaritans and the Jews of that day disliked one another. The Samaritans particularly disliked pilgrims going to worship at Jerusalem, for they had a small temple on Mount Gerizim, just outside their capital city of Samaria. They held that this was the proper place to worship God since it had first been established as a holy place by Abraham many centuries before Solomon built the temple at Jerusalem.

A few years before Jesus was born any band of Jewish pilgrims daring to go through Samaria would have been attacked by the Samaritans, robbed, and perhaps killed. But since the Romans had taken over the whole country of Palestine of which the provinces of Galilee, Samaria, and Judea were parts, Roman soldiers patrolled the roads,

16

Jerusalem today. Some of the present-day buildings date back hundreds of years. *Photo by Adelbert Bartlett*

and the Samaritans did not often fight the pilgrims. But the pilgrims from Nazareth were taking no chances of a sneak attack when the Roman soldiers did not happen to be around.

Jesus and his boy friends would have liked to be up front with the scouting party but they were told to stay in the central group. Most of the afternoon the band of pilgrims marched along without anything happening and the boys were growing a little weary of staying close to the central group. But late in the day a cloud of dust could be seen up the road behind them. Soon the men in the rear were shouting that a band of horsemen were overtaking them. The crowd of pilgrims grew tense. Could this be Samaritan bandits coming to rob them?

Quickly the group moved off the road. The women were put in a small group with the pack animals just outside them. The men drew up in a circle around the women and the animals. Every man was armed with a club or spear. Even the boys were given short, stout clubs and told to stand just behind the men. It would take a strong robber band to harm a group as large as this.

Drawn up so, they waited for whatever might happen. The dust cloud grew nearer and now the sound of horses' hoofs could be heard on the hard, dry road. The first of the horsemen appeared around a bend in the road. Soon others appeared. There were nearly a dozen in all, a band large enough to give real trouble. Jesus could feel the fear and excitement in those about him. A few of the women were crying softly.

The horsemen came on slowly, their horses at a walk. Were they friend or foe? As they drew closer the pilgrims could see they were dressed in Samaritan clothing and they prepared for the worst. But the horsemen rode slowly by without speaking or scarcely looking at the pilgrims, and everyone was beginning to breath more easily when

18

a shout arose from the scouts up front. More horsemen were approaching from that direction.

Just then the horsemen up front rode between the pilgrims and the sun and its rays glistened on their polished shields. A shout of relief broke from the throats of the pilgrims, for these were mounted Roman soldiers wearing the bright and shining armor of the mighty Roman Empire. No doubt the Samaritans had also seen the soldiers and, if they had planned to attack the pilgrims, changed their plans, for they would not dare with the Romans so near. The pilgrims knew they were safe. The men dropped their clubs. The women ceased their crying and the group broke out from the tight circle it had formed.

Since it was now nearly sundown, the pilgrims decided to make camp for the night where they were. Jesus began at once to search for wood for the campfire. The women unloaded the cooking pots off the pack animals and began to prepare the evening meal.

Meanwhile the Roman soldiers rode by. They stopped a few minutes to exchange friendly greetings with some of the men and told them that they would camp that night about a mile farther along the road and that if any trouble arose, they would be ready to help.

Tired and hungry as the pilgrims were, they did not begin their evening meal until the rabbi had called them together for a period of worship. When Joseph was chosen to read from the Torah, Jesus was very proud, for this was a high honor given only to the men who were considered spiritual leaders in the group.

How good supper tasted to Jesus after a long day of marching! The smell of burning wood and cooking food made it taste better. He ate until his mother laughingly told him he would burst if he ate any more.

That night about the campfires the talk of the men was not about wild animals but about Samaritans and particularly the Romans. Glad as the men had been to see the Roman soldiers that afternoon, none of them seemed to have a good word for them tonight, and Jesus was surprised at the sudden change.

"Why do our people hate the Romans so much?" he asked Joseph when he had a chance.

"I do not hate them, Son," Joseph answered. "I do not think God wants us to hate anyone. But some of our people do hate them. The Romans have taken over our country and our pride has been hurt. We want to run our own country. The Romans make us pay taxes to them and we do not like it. But I have heard my father tell how our own Jewish kings taxed us even more when they were ruling our country. We want to be free but we do not seem to know how to live as free men."

Jesus was not sure he understood all of this but he listened to what the men were saying.

"When the Christ comes, he will drive the Romans out and make us free once more," one of the men said.

"Do you think he is ever coming?" asked another man. "Seems as if we have waited long enough."

"I'm sure he will come soon," someone said. "We can't wait much longer."

"I wonder what he will be like," said the first man. "How can we be sure that he really is the Christ?"

A fourth man now joined in the discussion. "I think he will be a great warrior like David or Judas Maccabaeus. When he wins some battles, we will know who he is."

The rabbi next broke in and said, "We must remember that whoever the Christ is, he will first of all be a man of God. The prophets plainly teach us that. He may be a warrior, but he also may be a teacher and a man of peace."

"How can a teacher and a man of peace ever drive out the Romans?" the fourth man said almost angrily.

20

"I do not know," answered the rabbi. "I know only that scriptures say he will be a man of God."

The men were still arguing this point when Jesus fell asleep and he did not hear what they finally decided, if anything. On the march next day his mind returned to the subject. He pondered long and hard about God's Messiah to his people. Finally he forgot it in the excitement of seeing so many new and strange sights along the way.

When they came to the province of Judea (jew-dee′ah) they knew that the capital city of Jerusalem was not far away. By sundown they reached a village only two miles from the city itself. Here, on a hillside, they made a permanent camp, setting up tents and building ovens out of stones. Most of the pilgrims would spend the next week at this campsite, going into the city by day and returning to the camp at night. Joseph, Mary, and Jesus, however, did not plan to remain at the camp, as they had relatives in the city with whom they were to stay. Jesus wished that he might take along some of the boys in the camp with whom he had had so much fun on the trip but he knew that every house in the city was crowded with guests and that there would not be room for any more in the home of his host.

Next morning Jesus was up early, as was his custom, helping to light the campfires. As the sun came up, it cleared away a fog that had gathered in the little valley between the campsite and the city. Jesus stood enchanted by the view as the fog lifted higher and higher. First, the walls of the city began to appear, higher and thicker than he had imagined them. In those days all large cities were protected by big stone walls built all around them to keep out the armies of other nations. Gates were made here and there in the walls and people could enter or leave the city only through these.

21

Since the campsite was high on the mountainside, Jesus could see over the walls into the city itself as the fog arose. Tall buildings seemed to be everywhere. There were so many he could not begin to count them all. Far across the city a snow-white building began to appear and the sun glistened from its golden roof. He held his breath at the beauty of it. Without anyone telling him, he knew what this building must be—God's holy temple, the very place where God was supposed to dwell. He had been dreaming for months of worshiping in the temple and now here it lay in plain view. He was so thrilled a chill crept up his back and made him shiver in the morning coolness. But if he could have known all the shock and heartbreak that temple would bring to him in the next week and in the years to come, he would not have been so happy.

Map of Palestine

The outline map of Palestine at the beginning of this chapter shows where Jesus grew to manhood and lived throughout his life. The map shows the Sea of Galilee, the Jordan River, the Dead Sea, and the region between these and the Mediterranean Sea. It was in this region that Jesus lived, worked, preached, and taught.

2.

The Great City

AS SOON AS BREAKFAST was over, Jesus and his parents packed up and set out for the city of Jerusalem. It was only a short walk and they soon came to a great wooden gate that opened into the city. Here Jesus received his first shock about life in Jerusalem. He had always thought of it as God's holy city and supposed that everyone who lived there must be very religious and very happy.

Lined up on both sides of the gate were dozens of the poorest, unhappiest-looking people he had ever seen. Some were crippled, some blind, and all were dressed in dirty rags. They held out their hands to all who passed by and cried out for gifts of money and food. Each one seemed to try to cry louder than the others so that together they made a terrible noise with their screaming. Jesus had visited the poor in Nazareth and had carried them baskets of food sent by his parents, but he had never seen people who looked as poor as these or who screamed as loudly for help. He was deeply shocked and a question arose in his mind: Why should anyone who lived in God's city be so poor and unhappy as these seemed to be?

His young heart went out to them and he would have given them every bit of money he had if Joseph had not stopped him. This, too, came as a shock, for Joseph had always before encouraged him to share with poor people.

Once inside the gate and away from the beggars, Joseph explained: "Jerusalem is full of beggars, Son. Some are in real need and some are merely trying to get your money. You cannot give to them all, for that would take a cartload of money. You may choose one or two you think are in real need and help them. But you must save some of your money to feed yourself or you will become a beggar, too."

"But if they are hungry, I do not want to eat!" Jesus cried.

"I understand how you feel and am glad you want to give but God expects you to use your money wisely. He expects you to give to some of them but he knows you do not have enough to give to all. But there is something you can give each one of them and you will never run out."

"What is that?" Jesus asked eagerly.

"You can give them love and kindness; they are lonely as well as poor and crippled. The priests have told them that they are in need because they have sinned and God is punishing them. They think no one loves them, not even

God. You can love them and tell them that God loves them, for I am sure he does, and that will make them happier than a bag full of money."

Jesus did not answer, for as they moved through the street other things caught his attention. The street was much narrower than it had looked from the mountainside and it was crowded with people and animals. A train of a dozen camels, each heavily loaded, came toward them, bells tinkling. A man walked in front of the train shouting for people to clear the way. Jesus and his parents stood close to the wall of a house as the camels passed, almost touching them. The narrow street shut out the cool mountain wind and it was hot and steamy. The smell of animals, of garbage which had been thrown in the streets for the dogs to eat, of people who needed a bath mixed with the hot air made Jesus almost ill.

Farther along the street a tired old donkey had fallen down and his master was beating him with a whip to make him get up. A load of grain was tied to the donkey's back and Jesus could see at a glance that the load was too heavy for the animal. He longed to reach out and loosen the burden. But he was learning fast. This was the way of the city and there was nothing he could do about it, at least not now. He felt hot anger rising within him. This was not the way it should be in God's holy city.

The journey through the city was slow because of the narrow, crowded streets, but finally Joseph, Mary and Jesus arrived at the home of their hosts and were shown to a large room. After a good dinner they unpacked their few clothes and made ready for the night, for the sabbath would begin at sundown and no work could be done then.

Jesus went with his mother and the woman of the house to help carry water from the nearest fountain and here it was that Jesus learned why there were so many dirty people in the city. Water was scarce and hard to get. They trudged through more narrow streets, then went down a long flight of stone steps to a place where water flowed out of an underground tunnel into a pool. They went single file down the steps as there was a steady stream of water carriers coming up. They were women, except for some slaves, for carrying water was thought to be women's work in those days. Some of the women were old and tottered under the heavy water jars they balanced on their heads. Now and then there were men who had heavy rings in their ears and wore only a thin cloth about their waists.

When Jesus inquired who these were Mary whispered that they were slaves belonging to wealthy families. Jesus shuddered at the sight but said no more.

At the bottom of the steps they had to wait in a long line until they could fill their water jars at the pool. It took them an hour to get back to the house. "No wonder," thought Jesus, "the people find it hard to keep clean in this city."

On the sabbath Jesus went with his parents and their hosts to one of the many synagogues in the city. Like the one in Nazareth, only much larger, it was clean and quiet inside. Jesus proudly went with Joseph to the men's side of the large room. A wall ran through the middle of the room and the women, girls, and small boys sat out of sight on the other side of this. A rabbi with a fine, clear voice led the prayers. An important-looking man who sat in one of the front seats arose and read the scripture lesson from a long scroll which the rabbi handed him. When Jesus inquired later who this well-dressed man was, he was told that he was a Pharisee (fair'i-see) and president of the synagogue.

Early the next morning Jesus and his parents set off for the temple where they were to spend the day. It was not far but travel was slow, for many people were going to the temple. This was the beginning of the Passover week and Jews from all over the world had come to Jerusalem for the yearly observance. There were crowds everywhere.

The temple, like the city, was surrounded by a stone wall, only it was not as high. Jesus and his parents passed through a wide gate in the east side of the wall. All about the gate were crowds of beggars. There must have been hundreds of them crying "Give! Help! Alms!" Their cries filled the air until talk was impossible. Jesus began to understand what Joseph had meant about them. He picked out a blind man and a crippled boy and to each of these he gave a coin.

Inside the gate was a courtyard. It was very large and more like a field than a court. Another stone wall surrounded this. It was the court of the Gentiles (jen'til) and anyone might come in here. The Jews believed that Gentiles—all persons who were not Jews—were unclean and would not permit them to go any closer to the temple than this court. Along the walls of this court were booths or stalls where all kinds of things were being sold. It was more like a fair than a place of worship.

The family from Nazareth passed through this court into the Court of the Women. Not only were the Gentiles not allowed inside the temple area, neither were the women. They could come no closer than this special court for them. Here were more stalls and more things being sold. Here also were the places where offerings could be made and sacrificial animals bought. Here the rich Jews purchased oxen, or beef cattle. Others who could not pay the high price of an ox, bought sheep. These would later be used as burnt offerings on the altar of sacrifice inside the temple area. Ordinary people like Jesus' parents could afford neither an ox nor a sheep, so they bought a dove. The dove would not be used as a burnt offering but would be given its freedom and allowed to fly away. Joseph gave the dove he bought to Jesus to release. It was tame and sat on Jesus' hand as he petted it. He noticed that it had one bright blue feather over its right eye. He had to give it a little push before it would fly away and then it flew only to the wall of the court where several other doves had alighted.

Leaving Mary in the court of the women, Jesus and Joseph went into the next court. Here stood the temple. It was not a large building, but it was a beautiful one. Its walls were made of glistening white marble. Over the end of the building a grapevine made of pure gold seemed to grow. Each leaf and bunch of grapes were so carefully made they looked real, except for their golden color. The east end of the temple was open like a porch and here the priests and choirs of singers stood to conduct the worship services. The worshipers stood in an open court in front of the porch. Jesus found a place in the crowd of worshipers where he could see the priests, but he could not hear what they were saying. The screams of the beggars at the gates and the shouts of the merchants selling their wares drowned out the prayers of the priests and spoiled the chanting of the choirs.

So this was the great temple he had dreamed about! The place where God himself was supposed to be! It was a pretty building. But who could find God here among all this noise and confusion? Jesus was deeply shocked and he wanted to run out of the temple courts, never to return.

But there were duties he must attend to first. Now that he was 12 he was supposed to pay a temple tax. Just how much this tax was no one knows but it was not large. We will suppose that it was about 25 cents in our money. But Jesus soon learned there was a catch to it which made it cost him much more. He had only Roman money, the kind used throughout the country for ordinary purchases. But the chief priest had ruled that Roman money was unclean and could not be used in the temple. Only ancient Jewish or Hebrew money could be used there. This kind of money could be had only at the temple where moneychangers charged a high price for it. Thus in order to buy 25 cents worth of Hebrew coins with which to pay his tax, Jesus had to lay down more than a dollar's worth of Roman money. This seemed almost like stealing to him and kindled anger within him.

That night Jesus did not sleep well. He kept thinking about the beggars, the dirty, thin-faced children in the streets, the slaves with the rings in their ears, and the noise at the temple.

As Jesus returned to the temple the next day, he stopped to watch people buying doves as his parents had done the day before. He loved to watch them being released from their dirty coops into the bright blue sky. Here was something in the temple he thought seemed good. Then all at once he froze in horror. He moved up closer so that he could not be mistaken. The dove that had just been purchased by a man and his wife had a bright blue feather over its right eye. The man gave it to his wife and the dove sat on her hand and she had to give it a little push to make it fly away. Then it alighted on the wall just as it had the day before. There could be no mistake about it. It was the same dove Jesus had set free. Evidently it was trained, as were the other doves, to come back to the coop at night so it could be sold over again each day.

Was everything about the temple false? Tears stung his eyes and to hide them he wandered away, not caring where he went. Ashamed at the things he had seen, he wished he were back as a little boy again in Nazareth.

Sometime later Jesus came to what was known as Solomon's Porch at the back of the temple. It was quieter, and groups of people sat here and there around a rabbi who was teaching the Torah (Old Testament) to whoever would listen. Jesus stopped at two of these groups and listened half-heartedly. Then he joined another group. This rabbi was different. He was talking not just about the Torah but about the God of the Torah and how people ought to serve him. Jesus listened intently. Here was a man who could help him with the questions that troubled him. When the rabbi had finished speaking, he invited his listeners to ask questions. There were so many questions that Jesus had to wait a long time to ask his, but finally his turn came.

"Why is there so much noise in God's house when it should be a house of prayer?" he asked.

The rabbi sat for a moment in silence and all the men in the group turned and looked at Jesus. Finally the rabbi spoke. "That is a great question from such a young lad," he said. "The answer is not an easy one to find. Let us discuss it together."

But before the discussion got very far, it was time for Jesus to go. He had come alone to the temple and had promised to be back at the house an hour before sunset. The next morning he came early to the place where the rabbi taught and this time he brought Joseph with him. All day long they sat and studied under the rabbi, hearing him and asking him questions. As they were about to leave for the night, the rabbi came over and spoke to Joseph.

"That is a very bright son you have there," he said. "I should like to have him stay here in the temple with me so I can have longer to talk to him!"

"Thank you," said Joseph. "Jesus does have a good mind and we are honored by your invitation. I will talk to his mother and if it is all right with her the boy may visit you —that is, if he would like it."

"Oh, I would love it," Jesus cried.

So it was that the next day Jesus brought his bed roll prepared to spend the night with his new-found friend. He was happy. His trip to Jerusalem was going to be a good one after all. Now the hours flashed by so rapidly the

A street scene in present-day Jerusalem. The people still continue some ways of living as they were in the time of Jesus.

Photo by Marie Mattson of Black Star

day was gone before he realized it. That night he talked long after supper with the kindly rabbi. Other rabbis came by and joined in the talk. Jesus soon found himself in a circle of teachers hearing them and asking them questions. He wanted to know if they thought God lived only in the dark, curtained-off space at the back of the temple. The rabbis could not agree about the matter. Some thought God did. Others thought God could be found anywhere. Jesus knew he had talked to God out on the hills above Nazareth. And the Torah plainly taught that the holy of holies was God's dwelling place.

Then there were other questions which Jesus asked them. Why were there so many beggars and sick people? Why must they be so poor and lonely? Did not God care for them? Had they done some awful thing that had made God forget about them? The rabbis could not answer his questions. They read and reread long passages from the Torah and still the answers did not come. Jesus remembered the passage from the prophet Isaiah:

> The Spirit of the Lord GOD is upon me,
>   because the LORD has anointed me
> to bring good tidings to the afflicted;
>   he has sent me to bind up the broken-
>   hearted,
> to proclaim liberty to the captives,
>   and the opening of the prison to those
>   who are bound;
> to proclaim the year of the LORD's favor.
>
> —Isaiah 61:1-2

What was the prophet trying to say? Who was to preach to the poor? Who was to set the slaves free? None of them seemed to know.

The night wore on and the candles in the room began to flicker. Some of the candles went out so the rabbis decided to end their discussion.

32

The next day passed just as fast, as Jesus thought about answers to his questions; yet he was not sad about it now, for he felt that there were answers somewhere near. He trembled with the excitement of being so near and yet so far away from discovering them.

That afternoon Jesus had to leave his teacher when Joseph came for him because this was the night for the yearly feast of the Passover which families always ate together. Back at the home of his hosts the women had been busy all day preparing the supper they were to eat.

A lamb had been roasted whole over a charcoal fire for many hours. Flat cakes had been baked and a special preparation of bitter herbs prepared. Everything had to be done in just a certain way since the Torah told just how the meal was to be fixed. Other guests had come to the house for the Passover meal. Everyone stood up for the prayers before and after the meal. All this was done to help people remember the meaning of the Passover.

It was now several hundred years since God had led the Jewish people, then called Hebrews, out of Egypt and up to their present home in Palestine. The night the people began that long trip under the leadership of Moses they had all eaten a meal of roast lamb, dry bread, and bitter herbs—good food for marching. Each spring from that time on, the Jews commemorated God's protection of those who fled from Egypt. One part of the observance was the Passover meal such as Jesus had with his parents and their friends.

Jesus thought long about this and wondered if God would again free people from slavery if only a man like Moses would arise to teach and lead them. This was something else he must talk over with the rabbis at the temple. He had only one more day, for the pilgrims would start back toward Nazareth the morning after the sabbath.

33

In order to have more time with the rabbis, Jesus begged that he might spend the sabbath day in the temple court, sleep there that night, and come directly to the camp outside the city on the morning the pilgrims were to leave. His mother did not like the idea, but Joseph thought Jesus was old enough to be trusted. He told him he could do as he wished but that he must be at the camp bright and early.

So, early on the sabbath morning Jesus returned to the temple. For once it was quiet and prayerful. He joined in the worship in front of the temple, then went to Solomon's Porch where the teachers were to be found. All day long and far into the night they talked and talked. They read passage after passage from the Torah and from other sources. Jesus was getting some answers to his questions but not enough. When would God send someone to help his people? Whom would God send? Every teacher seemed to have a different idea. Jesus had to have more than an idea. He had to find out, for now there was a thought growing in his mind—suppose he, Jesus, were the one chosen of God to lead his people. He laughed at himself for having such an idea—he, a 12-year-old boy from the little town of Nazareth. But the idea was there and it kept coming back. Suppose he were the one!

Jesus slept little that night and when he did, he dreamed of hungry children, blind beggars, and slaves with rings in their ears. Suppose he were the one to set the captives free, to restore sight to the blind, to feed the hungry. How would he know? How would God speak to him? He had to find out.

Next morning everything else was forgotten. He ate no breakfast. He even forgot to wash. He woke up his rabbi friend before daylight to ask him the questions that had been with him all night. Hours flew by. Night came again. The next day Jesus had not once thought of the trip home.

Suddenly he heard a woman crying and calling out his name. It was his mother, and for a moment he thought she must be ill. Then it came to him what he had done. He had forgotten to keep his promise to meet them at the camp.

Joseph and Mary had gone to the camp the morning after the sabbath where a great crowd of people was moving out of the city. It was not possible to find anyone in such a crowd. Joseph was sure Jesus was somewhere in the crowd, so he and Mary walked all day long back toward Nazareth. Not until they made camp at night were all the people from Nazareth able to get together and when they checked up, Jesus was nowhere to be found. No one had seen him anywhere. Mary was wild with grief but Joseph only frowned a little. He was sure he knew where to find the boy.

Early next morning Joseph and Mary turned back toward Jerusalem and by late afternoon had reached the temple. They were sure they would find him here with the rabbis. He had been so interested in talking with them. When Jesus heard his mother crying, he ran to meet her in the Court of the Women.

As Mary caught sight of her son coming through the gate, she stopped her crying, but she did not run to him. There was something about the boy that made her look at him in wonder. About him there seemed to be a light she had seen before. She remembered the night a messenger from God had told her she was to be the mother of this boy. There had been a light about the messenger's face and it was like the light in Jesus' eyes. She remembered, too, the night he was born and how the stars had shone with light like this.

She wanted to run to her son and hold him in her arms, but something held her back. Somehow he was not her little boy any more. There was something of God in his face, something that made her pause and wonder in her heart what kind of child this was that God had given her. But she did manage to scold him gently for what he had done and the answer he gave her only set her heart to wondering still more.

"Did you not know that I must be in my Father's house?"

The Seder Plate

The Seder plate at the beginning of this chapter is a symbol of the Jewish Passover Feast. It is observed every year in late March or early April by Jewish families. It is in remembrance of the night when the Hebrews, led by Moses, fled from slavery in Egypt. The main service during the annual Passover is a meal called Seder which is eaten in the home. The kinds of food shown on the Seder plate were the foods the Hebrews ate before they made their flight from Egypt. Jesus and the disciples were observing the Passover meal when he instituted the Lord's Supper.

36

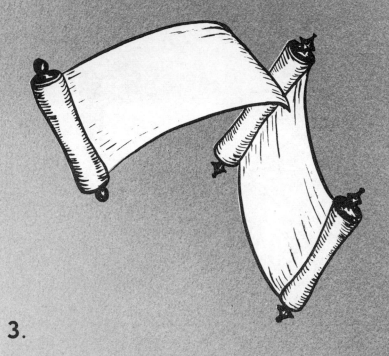

3.

From Boy to Man

WHEN JESUS RETURNED to Nazareth, he wanted more than ever to learn everything he could at the synagogue school, for now he believed that God had some great use for his life and he must be as well trained as possible. He read the Old Testament over and over until he knew much of it from memory.

The 18 years Jesus spent in Nazareth from the time he was 12 until he was 30 years old are known as the silent years, for little is known of what he did, but we can be sure that he studied and became familiar with the

history of his people. He came to know about David, greatest king of his nation. It was David who united the 12 tribes of the Hebrews into one nation and made Jerusalem the capital city. David served as king for many years and after him Solomon, his son, became king and built the first temple in Jerusalem. After Solomon's death the 12 tribes split apart. Ten of the tribes set up a new capital city at Samaria. This nation of 10 tribes is called "Israel" (iz'ra-ĕl) in much of the Old Testament. The other two tribes remained loyal to Jerusalem, and are known as Judah in the Old Testament. These two nations were often at war with one another or with a neighboring nation.

Seven hundred years before Jesus was born the city of Samaria was destroyed by the Assyrians (ă-sir'ians) and the nation of Israel disappeared. Judah lived on, but about 150 years later the city of Jerusalem and Solomon's temple were destroyed by the Babylonians. Seventy years later the temple was rebuilt and the walls of the city repaired. The people of Judah were now called "Judeans" and this name was soon shortened to "Jews."

For more than 300 years after this the Jews were ruled by foreign nations, but in the year 167 B.C. (before Christ) they revolted and became a free nation almost as great as they had been in the days of David.

All this came about in a thrilling way. A man called Judas Maccabaeus revolted when a foreign king commanded that he and his people worship an idol. With a small but very brave army he defeated the much larger army of the foreign king. This Judas did by means of a

◄ During his early life Jesus worked in the carpenter shop with Joseph.

trick. When the king came after him with a large army, Judas and his men hid in the mountains. The king made camp and sent a small army into the mountains to find Judas. In the meantime Judas marched his men by secret roads right to the king's main camp and attacked it by night. The king's men thought Judas had defeated the small army sent after him. Therefore, he must have a larger army than they had supposed. They took to their heels and ran away from the camp. Judas calmly took over the camp and waited until he saw the small army returning to tell their king they could not find Judas. Then he had his men set fire to the camp. When the small army saw this, it, too, ran away.

Judas, his two brothers, their sons and grandsons served as kings over the Jewish nation for more than a hundred years. It was a happy time for the Jews. They had their own nation once again. They were a free people.

Then, about 40 years before Jesus was born, Herod, a distant relative of the family of Judas Maccabaeus, managed to get himself appointed king. He was a strong but wicked man. To make his position secure he killed all of Judas' other relatives. This made the people angry and they tried to take the kingdom away from Herod but he went to the Roman government. The Romans sent in soldiers to protect Herod, but they did not stop there. Before the Jews were aware of it, the Romans had taken over their country. They were back under a foreign nation again with scarcely a battle being fought.

The Jews naturally hated the Romans who had taken away their country and they hated Herod who had sold out their freedom. To try to win back their good will, Herod rebuilt the temple, making it larger and of the most expensive materials. It was to this temple that Jesus came to worship at the age of 12.

Some among the Jews, known as Zealots (zel'uts), were

40

Nazareth as it looks today. It was here that Jesus grew to manhood. The spire in the right foreground is constructed over the traditional site of Joseph's carpenter shop. *Photo by Adelbert Bartlett*

always looking for a new Judas to arise and drive the Romans out. At least one of Jesus' disciples was a Zealot.

Another group of Jews, known as Pharisees, thought it impossible to defeat the Romans but sought instead to purify their religion of all foreign ideas. They urged their people to return to the Law given by Moses. Every rule and regulation must be carefully observed, they said. To break one little rule was as bad to them as the breaking of all the Law. They even went so far as to say that a doctor could not help the sick on the sabbath day since this would be work and work was forbidden on this day. Jesus had a great deal of trouble with these people as we shall later see.

Both of these groups believed that if ever they were to be delivered from Roman rule, it would have to be through some divine leader sent to them by God. The Zealots believed that he would be a great warrior like David or Judas Maccabaeus and, through wisdom given him by God, he would defeat the Romans in a mighty battle. The Pharisees believed he would be less of a warrior and more a man of God. They held he would drive out the Romans but were not sure how he would do it. This hoped-for leader was called the "Messiah" (me-sī′a) in the Jewish language and "the Christ" in the Greek language. Both terms meant the same thing. This "messianic hope," as it was called, was not a new idea. It had been a dream in the hearts of the Jews for many centuries. They looked eagerly to the day when the Messiah would come.

Another group of Jews, known as the Sadducees (sad′-u-sees), thought the best thing to do was to get along with the Romans. The Sadducees were mostly wealthy businessmen and they had found that trade with the Romans was good business.

It is believed that Joseph died during the years when

42

Jesus was growing from boy to man, for he is never mentioned again as living. Jesus probably helped his mother support the family and this may be one reason why he waited until he was 30 years old to begin preaching. He loved family life and was kind and thoughtful of his own family. He had younger brothers and sisters but it is not known how many. Mark 6:3 states that he had four brothers and some sisters. No doubt Jesus helped to care for these after the death of Joseph.

During these years Jesus must have spent many hours thinking and praying about God's purpose for his life. He formed the habit of going out alone before the beginning of the day's work to talk to God about that purpose. He became more and more convinced that God had chosen him for some great work. But what was that work and how was he to begin it?

Then, one day, the call came, not in a flash of fire from the sky but in a message delivered by a friendly neighbor. The neighbor had made a trip to hear a preacher who was becoming famous throughout the country. The preacher was known as John the Baptist. As the neighbor told of the things John preached, the strange light came again into the eyes of Jesus.

"I must go and hear him for myself," said Jesus, and he laid aside the carpenter work he had been doing, never to take it up again.

A Special Note to the Reader

How can we say that Jesus did and thought the things we have mentioned so far in this book? The Bible tells us only a little about his birth and about the trip he made when he was 12. Is all the rest of this just imagination? In a way it is and in another way it is not. Although we have no record telling us just what he did all these years, we can read about the time in which he lived in books other than the Bible, for many such books exist. We can learn how other people lived in that time. Then we can imagine how Jesus

43

must have lived, how he got his education, how he traveled, and what he saw along the way.

This book is written to help young people understand two things about Jesus: first, that he was and is the Son of God and the Savior of the world and, second, that he was a warm, lovable human being, knowing hunger and thirst, joy and sadness like any other normal boy and young man. The Bible shows him plainly as both the Son of God and the Son of man. Young Christians should see him both as Christ the Savior and as Jesus, the bold Galilean.

The Scrolls

The symbol of the scrolls at the beginning of this chapter is used to illustrate the schooling of Jesus. Every Jewish boy at that time was required to attend classes held in the nearby synagogue where the studying was done from scrolls. The scrolls were often made of dried sheepskin in sheets from 9 to 11 inches high and 5 or 6 inches wide, sewed together to make a long strip which was rolled around a stick. The reader held the roll in his left hand and with his right hand wound it around another stick, or just rolled it up. Most of the Jewish families had a few scrolls which were kept as we keep the family Bible. These were usually stored together in a jar or chest.

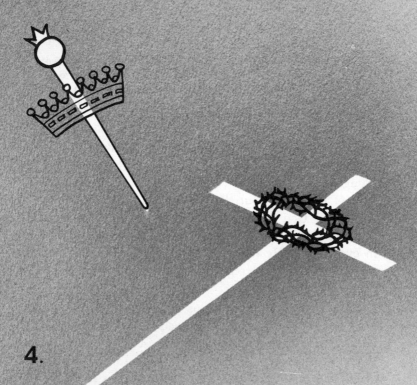

4.

Night in the Wilderness

THE TALL FIGURE of a man paused in the early morning light where two roads came together. He gazed first down one road then the other as if undecided which he should take. Slowly his large, well-formed head lifted toward the sky and his lips moved in wordless prayer revealing strong, hard muscles in his cheeks and neck. His black, deep-set eyes seemed to drill holes in the air as if they were hungry to see more than ordinary eyes could see. His large, strong hands reached out as if they would grasp something beyond their reach. The

45

prayer lasted only a moment then the man stood as if listening for some sound in the morning quiet. This, too, lasted but a moment and then he struck out on the road to the right with long, steady strides like a man who knew where he was going but who had a long way to go and must save his strength for the miles ahead.

Jesus was on his way to meet John the Baptist and he had chosen to take the short road through Samaria even though he was alone and the Samaritans were bitter enemies of the Jews. But the choice was not his alone. He had asked God to help him choose the road he should take, for it had become his custom to ask God's guidance in everything. He now felt it was God's will for him to go through Samaria regardless of any danger along the way.

He passed many Samaritans on the road that day but none offered to harm him. To each he gave a warm smile and a friendly greeting and the surprised Samaritans were quick to return his greeting. He slept soundly and unafraid that night wrapped in a long coat his mother had made for him. Late the next day he arrived at the place where John was preaching.

John the Baptist was different from Jesus. Jesus was tall and neatly dressed in the clothing of the day; John was short and dressed in the skins of wild animals. Jesus was smooth-shaven except for a small, carefully trimmed beard; John's black whiskers covered his face.

John lived in a camp on the Jordan River. Here he preached to such people as would come to hear him. When Jesus arrived at the camp, John the Baptist was preaching to a small crowd seated on the ground before him. Jesus sat down at the edge of the crowd and listened. John's words burned like fire. He warned his listeners that they must repent of their sinful ways or God would destroy them.

46

"Even now the ax is laid to the root of the trees; every tree therefore that does not bear good fruit is cut down and thrown into the fire."

—Luke 3:9

Jesus listened and understood what John meant. As the farmer cuts down and burns a tree that does not bear fruit, just so God would destroy a nation of people who failed to live good lives. Jesus thought of the money-changers in the temple growing rich on their profits and of the slaves with the rings in their ears carrying heavy water jars up long flights of stairs.

After the sermon some of the people came to John, confessed their sins, and promised to lead a better life. These were baptized in the river by some of John's helpers.

Jesus spoke to John and they put their arms around one another as men friends often did in those days, for they were distantly related and had known one another since boyhood. They spent the rest of the day and much of the night talking together about God's will for their lives. Both men were convinced that they must give their lives fully to God and do whatever they felt he wanted them to do. Both were deeply concerned about the spiritual life of the Jewish people and felt that they must do what they could to help their people live better lives. John was sure the way to do this was to point out men's sins and to warn them about the coming judgment of God.

Jesus remained at John's camp for several days. Often he sat and watched the people as they listened to John. He could see shame and fear come into their faces as John told them about their empty, useless lives and warned them of God's judgment. He saw, too, something else there, a hunger for something more than John was telling them. It touched him deeply and Jesus prayed silently for each one. What was it they really needed?

47

Suddenly Jesus knew. After all these years of searching the answer came clear and plain. God had at last shown him the way. The people needed something more than the fear of God in their hearts. They needed to know him as Jesus knew him, as a loving heavenly Father who wanted to fill their hearts with joy, hope, courage, and peace.

Jesus had never had any desire to speak in public. He had been content to study, pray, and wait. Now a message burned in his heart. He wanted to shout the good news to everybody that God would give a new and wonderful life to anyone who would earnestly seek it. The slaves would be free of their slavery, the beggars would become rich in God's love, and, the wealthy, discovering that life was far more important than money, would lose their greed for gold.

It had been a long wait for God's message but Jesus was glad he had waited. Even yet he was not quite ready. He must find out how God wanted him to spread this great message.

That afternoon Jesus asked John to baptize him but John threw up his hands in protest:

"I need to be baptized by you, and do you come to me?"

But Jesus answered:

"Let it be so now; for thus it is fitting for us to fulfill all righteousness."

—Matthew 3:14-15

Then John led him out into the river and baptized him. As Jesus was wading back toward shore he stopped and lifted his head toward the sky. A wonderful thing happened to him. God spoke to him in clear, unmistakable words:

In those days Jesus came from Nazareth of Galilee and was baptized by John in the Jordan. (Mark 1:9.)

"This is my beloved Son, with whom I am well pleased."

—Matthew 3:17

The words echoed in his ears like thunder rolling along the high cliffs of the Jordan. Now he was sure. The idea that had come to his mind on his first visit to the temple had grown through the years. God had chosen him to be the new Moses to lead his people into a new way of life. Of that he had felt sure for some time now. But to be God's own beloved Son—did he dare think of himself as such? Moses had been a great leader and messenger, but he was to be more, God's beloved Son. David had been a great king but he was to be more, the Prince of heaven! Judas Maccabaeus had delivered his people from a foreign king, but he was to be the Savior of the world!

His mind was so full of the great ideas bursting upon it that Jesus walked like a man in a dream. John and his helpers spoke to him but he did not hear or answer them. He had to get away. Where, it did not matter, but he must be alone with God.

Someone put a bundle in his arms but he was not aware of it. He must walk, walk, walk.

How long or how far he walked he did not know. By nightfall he was far out in the desert. He unrolled the bundle in his arms. In it were his long coat and a leather canteen of water. He was grateful that John and his helpers had understood and had provided for his physical needs. He drank of the water and ate some of the dried fruits. But food and drink did not matter now. It mattered only that he might prove worthy of the trust God had given him.

For 40 days Jesus remained alone in the desert, thinking about his mission and how he would achieve it. Hour after hour he spent in prayer until his mind and heart and soul were full of the knowledge of God.

Slowly it came to him that as God's beloved Son and as Prince of heaven the world was at his feet. He could do anything he wanted to do with it. All at once he realized he was hungry. Could he have seen himself he would have realized that his once strong body was thin from lack of food. His hair was long and matted, his face covered with a wild growth of beard.

There came a thought to his mind. Why should the Prince of heaven go hungry? He saw about him round stones half buried in the sand. They looked like the loaves of bread his mother baked so well. He had but to speak and they would turn to bread.

Now he heard the tempter speaking sneeringly,

> "If you are the Son of God, command these stones to become loaves of bread."
>
> —Matthew 4:3

It would be so easy. Just a word would do it and the desert, as far as he could see, would be filled with bread. He thought of the beggars and all the other poor people he knew. How glad they would be to hear that the desert was filled with bread. They would rush out to him, eat their fill, proclaim him as their king and follow him wherever he went.

But was this God's way to save people from hunger? Just give them free food for the rest of their lives? From the passages he had memorized as a boy in the synagogue school there came to him a verse and he said it aloud:

> " 'Man shall not live by bread alone,
> but by every word that proceeds from
> the mouth of God.' "
>
> —Matthew 4:4

51

Jesus' early ministry was not always met with enthusiastic response. Read Luke 4:16-30 for the biblical account of the incident illustrated here.

This was God's answer to the temptation to take the easy way. God wanted his people to have bread, but he also wanted to feed their souls on great ideas. Bread alone would never be enough. It was love and life they were really hungry for and if they would love one another as God loved them, they would share their bread until there would be enough for all.

But would the people believe him if he were to tell them that? He thought of the great crowds in Jerusalem. Suppose he should go and say to them, "Love God with all your heart, do his will in your lives, love one another and there will be bread enough for all." Would they listen to him, a young man from Galilee? How could he make them believe him?

Again the tempter said:

"If you are the Son of God, throw yourself down; for it is written,
'He will give his angels charge of you,'

and

'On their hands they will bear you up, lest you strike your foot against a stone.' "

—Matthew 4:6

This would be the easy way to make the people listen and as the Son of God he could do it. He could jump off the temple, he could fly through the air, he could sit on a cloud and tell them they were God's chosen people as he was God's chosen Son. They would like that and they would listen.

Nearly everyone, he knew, wanted to feel important. Many of his Jewish friends would love it if he told them they were the special favorites of God. They would believe him if he were to say they were more important to

53

God than the Samaritans or the Romans. He could feed
their vanity, play upon their national pride and he would
be a great hero to them. He could say to them what the
tempter had said to him: " 'He will give his angels charge
of you.' God will take care of you, not because you are
good or worthy, but because of who you are. You are
important to God and other people are not. God will give
you special favors that he will not give to others, just because you demand that he do so. You can think of yourself as better than other people. You can say that you
are right and everybody else is wrong. God is on your
side and will fight against anyone you dislike."

Yes, many of his people would love a message like that
and would be eager to follow him. But he knew this was
not God's real message of love. He was being tempted to
be popular rather than honest. As God's Son he was to do
God's will even though this might not be the popular
way. He must show people that God loved all his children, that he had no favorites among them. He must not
yield to the temptation to ask special favors for himself
or his people. God, he knew, would help him, stand by
him, lead and direct him, and he dare not ask for more
than this. So he answered the tempter with another verse
he had memorized:

" 'You shall not tempt the Lord your God.' "

—Matthew 4:7

Then another thought came to him. As the Son of God
he could organize a small army, protect it from the spears
of other armies by divine power and conquer the world.
His people would be free from Rome and they would like
that. He could rule as a king in Jerusalem and he would
be the greatest and wisest king the world had ever known.
He could free every slave. He could force bad people to
live good lives. He could cause selfish people to become

unselfish. He could cure all the troubles of the world in no time.

This would be just the kind of Christ or Messiah many of the Jewish people were looking for. It was the kind of person they had made up their minds that they wanted God to send them, and they would accept him quickly. But were their ideas God's ideas? Did God want his Son to rule the world as a warrior-king?

During the 40 days in the wilderness Jesus had become sure that he was God's beloved Son and that, as such he was also the Christ, the Messiah. He was the Christ the people were looking for so earnestly. But what kind of Christ should he be? Their kind? One who would use God's power to force people to obey and follow him? It would be so much easier to make everyone believe in him rather than to wait for them to choose him of their own free will. It would be so much quicker, too. In a few weeks or months at the most, he could make everyone in the world believe on him and he could ever afterward rule the whole world with justice and mercy. It would be the easy way.

The temptation was strong. He wanted desperately to win the world quickly to God. He knew also that the tempter represented all the forces in the world that opposed God's rule. How nearly he had fallen into the trap! The easy way, that was not God's way.

Jesus stood up, his hair was uncombed and his clothes were ragged from his long stay in the desert but there was majesty in his being. He was every inch the Prince of heaven. Divine fire flashed from his eyes as he turned to the tempter and said:

> "Begone, Satan! for it is written,
> 'You shall worship the Lord your God
> and him only shall you serve.'"

> —Matthew 4:10

55

At last Jesus was ready. He knew for sure now that he was to tell the people the good news about God. It would not be easy, but somewhere he would find a few who would believe him. They would tell others and these would tell still others until all the world should know that he brought a message of life from God. It would be slow and hard but it was God's way. He realized he could not tell the people he was God's Son. That was something they must discover for themselves by the way he lived among them and by the things he taught them about God. Some would listen to him and some would laugh at him. But it did not matter, he was going God's way and God would be with him all the way.

He rolled up his coat and, weak as he was from hunger, struck out swiftly. There was much work ahead and he must be about it.

The Crowns, the Scepter and the Cross

The symbols at the beginning of this chapter represent choices which faced Jesus in his temptations. During his 40 days and nights in the wilderness, he had to determine the nature of his ministry. Should he take the way of kings and political power, or the way of love and the rule of God? The jeweled crown and scepter symbolize political power, which he rejected. The crown of thorns and cross symbolize the way he chose and through which he became the lord of life.

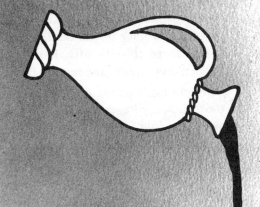

5.

Four Men and a Boat

ON THE WAY BACK from the desert to Nazareth, Jesus stopped along the way only long enough to get his hair trimmed and his clothes cleaned up.

Even then when he returned home, his mother, in the way of all mothers, looked anxiously at his thin cheeks and heaped the table at mealtime with the things he liked to eat. His brothers watched him out of the corner of their eyes as if he had some strange disease or was losing his mind. When he announced that he did not plan to return to his job in the family carpenter shop but intended to become a rabbi and travel from village to village teaching, they looked even more queerly at him.

Jesus knew it would be of no use to tell them what had happened to him. They had known him too long as the quiet, oldest brother in the family. But he was content to wait. He loved this friendly, hard-working family of his and hoped they would understand him.

He began his teaching and preaching quietly, going out to the smaller villages around Nazareth and talking to whomever would listen to him. Now and then he was invited to preach in a small synagogue on the sabbath day. But the people around Nazareth also knew him too well as the carpenter's son. They listened to him and liked his warm, friendly manner, but no one among them believed him.

After a few weeks Jesus went north to the country around the Sea of Galilee. Here the people were the most friendly of all. He was asked to speak in some of their largest synagogues, and crowds of people came to sit in his outdoor classes. The fishermen at the lake showed a great interest in him and at evening would gather on the beach to listen to him. Here Jesus met four young men whom he loved from the moment he met them. There were two sets of brothers, Simon and Andrew and James and John. Simon was the oldest of the four and was married. He was about the same age as Jesus. John was the youngest, being only about 20 years old.

Jesus spent a great deal of time with them talking to them about the good news of the gospel and he could see that they were beginning to believe him. It warmed his heart that he had found some real followers.

On his return to Nazareth, he realized that his work would be not only hard, it could be dangerous too, for shocking news came to him there. John the Baptist had

58

After this he went out, and saw a tax collector, named Levi
[Matthew], sitting at the tax office; and he said to him, "Fol-
low me." And he left everything, and rose and followed him.
(Luke 5:27-28.)

been arrested and thrown into prison. Jesus had expected people to be slow in believing. But would there be some who would fight against him as they had John? He realized that he was preaching a new kind of religion and that there would be some who would not like it. They would prefer the old religion just because it was old, and they might even fight against anyone who dared to suggest changes.

Suddenly he was aware that he had been moving too slowly. He must strike out quickly before the opposition should become too strong. He must preach in the great cities as well as the villages. He must have helpers, for he saw he could not do the work alone. Where would he get them? At once he thought of the four fishermen. With some training they would make fine helpers.

Meanwhile, the four fishermen had been talking things over. They were strong, freedom-loving men, and they hated the Romans who ruled them and made them pay taxes on every boatload of fish they sold. They longed for the Messiah who would rally the Jews and drive out the Romans. Could this Jesus be the man? He had a kingly way about him and he talked about a new kingdom, only he called it the kingdom of God.

John was the first to speak out about it. "I think he is the man," he said. "If he should issue a call to arms, I'm ready to go." He pulled out his fishing knife and flashed it about like an imaginary sword.

"I think we ought to go too," said Andrew to Simon. "But what about your wife?"

"You don't know my wife," Simon answered. "She hates the Romans more than I do and would be the first to urge me to go. But what would become of our boat?"

Suddenly they all fell silent, for every man admired that boat. It was the finest fishing craft on the lake and was their pride and joy. With her sail up she could split the waves faster than any boat about and when they plied the oars, she responded like a thing alive.

A few days later Jesus appeared at the lake. Simon and Andrew were putting out a shore net while James and John were some distance away helping their father, Zebedee, mend their nets. After a warm greeting Jesus helped the two brothers pull in their heavy net. Not a fish was to be found in it and they hung the net up to dry, then sat down in a shady place to talk. At once Jesus began to talk of his need for helpers. Then he laid a hand on Peter's wind-burned arm and said, "Follow me and I will make you become fishers of men." (Mark 1:17.)

Simon looked deeply into the eyes of Jesus; then, as if he could not quite bear what he saw there, turned his eyes away. Was this the man he had been looking for as his Christ and king? He stole another glance at him. He was tall enough and strong enough. Simon thought for a moment, "I would not want to get into a fight with him, but he does not seem to be the fighting type. He is gentle and kind and does not seem to want to harm anyone. How could he ever lead an army in battle?"

He looked at the lake, blue as only the Sea of Galilee can be, and at his boat tugging gently at her anchor as if anxious to be out and away across the dancing waves. Could he leave all this to follow a man he was not sure about? He stared for a long time at the sea and the boat. No, he decided, it was not for him. He was a fisherman born. His place was here by the sea.

He turned to give his answer to Jesus and his mouth fell open, for Jesus was walking off down the beach and beside him walked Andrew, his fisherman's coat under his arm. The two brothers had always done everything together and each understood the other well. Simon knew he was the one who usually decided what should be done with Andrew following along. He, Simon, was

61

the quick, strong one. If there was a load to be lifted or a sail to be brought about in the wind, he was the one to do it. Andrew was the slow, careful one. He did not get excited easily. His hand at the helm of the boat could keep her on course in the roughest of seas. Simon sometimes grew angry at his brother's slowness but he always felt safe and secure with him.

Now Andrew was going ahead of him. He had decided to follow Jesus. Should he trust Andrew's calm judgment above his own? He looked at the two men walking away from him. There was something kingly about the way this man Jesus walked. Simon picked up his coat from the sand, took one last, lingering look at the boat and called out, "Wait, Andrew, I'm coming, too."

Stopping by Zebedee's boat, Jesus issued the same call to James and John. They talked it over with their father and although he wanted them to stay with him, he was wise enough to let his sons make up their own minds about the matter. It took John only a few minutes to decide, and he was soon ready to follow Jesus. James took longer putting away this and that in the boat and stealing many a glance at his father. It was hard to leave him with the fishing business to look after alone. But the call of Jesus reached deep into James' heart, and after a while, he, too, left his father and the boat to follow the way of his inner heart.

After giving the four fishermen a few days to get ready for the trip Jesus set out with them on a speaking tour of the province of Galilee. Everywhere they went they found crowds of listeners, for Jesus spoke in a different way from the ordinary rabbi. It was the custom of the rabbis to argue about belief in God and about the proper kind of faith one should have about God. Jesus did not argue at all. He spoke of God as his Father and Friend who was near to him. He talked simply of what he knew about the rule of God, the kingdom that people could enter into at once by living according to God's laws of love. He told them over and over that a whole new life was open to them if they would only believe. The people were delighted by his speeches, for he was an excellent speaker, but few showed much belief.

Much of the time Jesus spent talking to the four fishermen whom he now called "disciples," which means students or pupils. He was preparing them as rapidly as possible for the time when they could also tell the people the good news of the kingdom.

At this time Jesus and his band of students or disciples turned southward toward Jerusalem. On the way they passed through Nazareth. Now that Jesus had become known as a teaching rabbi, he was invited to speak in the synagogue where he had studied and worshiped all his life. The whole town turned out to hear him and all his neighbors wondered what he would have to say.

When the time came for him to speak he was handed a scroll of the Book of Isaiah and he opened it to the passage that had meant so much to him as a boy. He read it slowly and carefully to the people.

" 'The Spirit of the Lord is upon me,
    because he has anointed me to preach good
        news to the poor.
    He has sent me to proclaim release to the cap-
        tives
    and recovering of sight to the blind,
    to set at liberty those who are oppressed,
    to proclaim the acceptable year of the Lord."

And he closed the book, and gave it back to the attendant, and sat down; and the eyes of all in the synagogue were fixed on him. And

he began to say to them, "Today this scripture
has been fulfilled in your hearing."

—Luke 4:18-21

By this Jesus was boldly saying that he was the Christ
for whom the people had been looking to free them from
their bondage. No one in Nazareth believed him. They
had known him all his life and he was just the carpenter's
son to them.

In anger the people in the synagogue put him out of
the city. Then they began shoving him toward the edge
of a cliff which was near the outskirts of town. They
were like an angry mob and they intended to throw him
down headlong. Just a few more feet and they would be
ready to cast him over.

Gathering all his strength he side-stepped the men who
were pushing him from behind and turned to face the
crowd. He stood a head taller than most of the men and
his shoulders were squared. The men stopped and
fell back a step or two. Jesus marched straight at them,
his face set, his eyes flashing. A pathway opened and he
walked through the crowd unharmed.

Rejoining his frightened disciples, he led them up the
road with never a backward look. He was fearless. No
man, or group of men, was going to turn him aside from
the mission to which he had dedicated himself. Already
the opposition had begun and there was much work to
be done.

As they were going along the road one day, a leper
ran up to Jesus, knelt before him in the road, and cried
out, "If you will, you can make me clean." (Mark 1:40.)

Jesus looked at him and pity filled his heart. White
scales covered the man's hands and some were on his
nose. Jesus knew how the terrible disease worked.
Slowly the man's fingers would dry up and drop off,

then his hands and, finally, his nose. He would be a horrible-looking creature, crippled, alone, friendless, but still he would go on living, for the disease killed its victims very slowly. Jesus knew it was God's will that all his children should have health and strength. Somewhere, he knew, God had a cure for this disease. But men were not looking for God's cure. They said the disease was punishment for some sin the man had committed and was good enough for him. Let the man be thrown out to live alone and finally die. What did they care as long as they did not catch his disease?

The sight of the man, his simple faith in Jesus' power to heal, was too much for Jesus. His hand went out to touch the man. Instantly the white scales disappeared. The man was well and strong again. Joy flooded through Jesus like music. God's power could save men from disease, but at once he knew the danger of what he had done. He was not a miracle worker but a messenger from God. He had good news to tell people. He knew the truth about God and with that truth men could find God's cures for many kinds of diseases. More than that, with this truth they could live good, happy, rich lives in spite of disease. Health was a fine thing to have, but to know and live in God's love was much more important.

So Jesus took the man aside and spoke to him. "See that you say nothing to any one," he told the man. Then he and his disciples left the place quickly.

But the man could not keep the story to himself. It was all too wonderful. From house to house it flew. Down the road it went with every traveler in the land. "There is a young prophet in Galilee who cured 10 lepers all at once." At Jerusalem another traveler told it this way, "There is a young prophet in Galilee who can cure all kinds of diseases. If he walks along the road and his shadow falls on the sick, they are made well at once. Why, I hear he has even raised the dead!"

In a few days the story was all over Galilee, and everywhere Jesus went people thronged about him until he could scarcely move. They would not listen to what he had to say. All they wanted was to see him perform a miracle.

Jesus' heart was heavy as he saw how the people put excitement above truth and health above God. But some few did listen to him and from these he chose some more disciples; Matthew, who left a good-paying job with the Roman government as tax collector; Philip, Bartholomew (Nathanael), Thomas, Thaddaeus, and another man by the name of James, the son of Alphaeus.

Arrived at Jerusalem, Jesus went to Solomon's Porch where he had once studied so earnestly as a boy. Now he was one of the teachers here and large crowds gathered around him. Some of the other rabbis tried to get him into long-winded arguments about minor questions, but he had no time to waste on such trifles. He talked constantly about life in the kingdom of God. All listened, for he held people spellbound, but only here and there did he find anyone who would believe in his message.

One of these was Judas Iscariot (ĭs-kar'i-ot), a strange, quiet young fellow from the desert country south of Jerusalem.

A second was another man named Simon. He is not to be confused with Simon, the fisherman, who was later called Peter. This Simon was a member of the revolutionary party known as Zealots, so called because they had a great zeal to drive out the Romans and free their country. They usually carried knives or swords hidden under their clothes and sometimes organized themselves into small, bandit gangs.

We can imagine Simon's thoughts when he became acquainted with Jesus. He must have asked himself many times if this Jesus was the divine leader for whom the

Zealots had been looking. Was he the promised Christ who would restore the kingdom of David and Judas? Could he organize and lead an army that could defeat the hated Romans? It must have been hard for Simon to decide. Jesus was not the kind of warrior-Messiah he had expected, yet there was something about the man that drew him.

At last Simon followed the way of his inner heart and threw in his lot with Jesus. This brought the number of disciples to 12 and the band remained at this number for many months.

These Twelve Jesus set out to train as his helpers but, since there were always crowds about, he found it difficult to spend much time alone with them. They still did not know much about the good news of the kingdom and they must understand it if they were to be his helpers. So he left Jerusalem and camped in the mountains near by. Here he organized the disciples into an orderly group. Judas was chosen as the treasurer. People were giving them more and more money and it must be used carefully since it was a sacred trust. With this money Judas would buy their food and such other things as they needed. Matthew was probably chosen as secretary to keep records of their work and of the things Jesus taught them. Peter, James and John became an inner council group representing the larger group in meetings with Jesus.

He was now ready to give them their instructions as teacher-helpers. He had them sit down on the mountainside about him and all day long talked with them.

Jesus described the person who would be in the kingdom, living under God's rule as:

He who is aware that he is not as upright as he
     wants to be and is striving continually to be better.
He who feels within himself the sorrows and disap-
     pointments of others.

67

He who recognizes the worth of others and does not
think himself better than they.

He who truly wants to know and do God's will.

He who is merciful toward others.

He who tries to live peaceably with his fellows and
to make peace among them.

He who does what is right even if his friends and
associates laugh at him and think him foolish.

He who continues to be kind and fair toward those
who do him harm.

Jesus wanted his followers to know that becoming a
citizen in God's kingdom required more than going
through certain ceremonies or obeying a set of rules.
What one thinks and feels must be in keeping with God's
purposes. Often Jesus told his followers that they must
be more upright than the Pharisees, who were very con-
scientious to do exactly what the law required, no more
and no less. By doing this they lost the very purpose of
the law.

As an example of what he meant, Jesus reminded his
hearers of the law against murder. He taught that it is
not enough to refrain from killing another, one should
not even hate or despise another, for out of this hatred
can grow thoughts and feelings which lead to murder.

Another example Jesus used was the ancient law about
requiring love for brothers and members of one's own
family and tribe with nothing said about loving those beyond the family or tribe. Jesus said that this was not
enough, but

"Love your enemies and pray for those who
persecute you, so that you may be sons of your
Father who is in heaven."

—Matthew 5:44b-45a

68

Seeing the crowds, he went up on the mountain,
and when he sat down his disciples came to him.
And he opened his mouth and taught them.
(Matthew 5:1-2.)

Over and over again Jesus emphasized that doing God's will meant more than good deeds, it meant inner goodness. He taught that those who would do God's will must be upright without parading their good deeds before their fellows. They must help others without calling everyone's attention to what they do. They must pray to God in private and not brag about how frequently or long they pray.

"Not every one who says to me, 'Lord, Lord,' shall enter the kingdom of heaven, but he who does the will of my Father who is in heaven."

—Matthew 7:21

He told them that everyone who heard and practiced his teachings was like a wise builder who erected a house on a rock, and the floods and winds came, but could not beat it down. Likewise everyone hearing his teachings and ignoring them was like a foolish man who built a house on sand, and the wind and rain beat against it until it collapsed.

All who heard Jesus speak these words were impressed and astonished, "for he taught them as one who had authority, and not as their scribes." (Matthew 7:29.)

The Cruse of Oil

The cruse of oil at the beginning of this chapter is a symbol of pouring out a blessing upon a person. Kings and priests were always anointed with oil as an honor and as a mark of consecration to their work. The word "Christ" is taken from the Greek word which means "anointed."

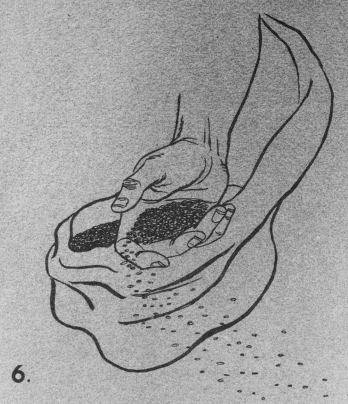

6.

The Lion Begins to Roar

THE FAME OF JESUS had now spread
throughout the country and everywhere he
went great crowds of people came out to see
him. He could no longer speak in the quiet
voice he had been using with smaller groups
but had to shout to be heard.

Therefore, he began to tell short, simple
stories that would explain to the people what
he meant by the kingdom of God. Over and
over again he told these stories known as
parables and people loved them.

One of the parables he told was to explain, more to
the disciples than to anyone else, why it was that in a
crowd of people listening to him some would believe and
some would not.

> That same day Jesus went out of the house
> and sat beside the sea. And great crowds gath-
> ered about him, so that he got into a boat and
> sat there; and the whole crowd stood on the
> beach. And he told them many things in par-
> ables, saying: "A sower went out to sow. And
> as he sowed, some seeds fell along the path, and
> the birds came and devoured them. Other seeds
> fell on rocky ground, where they had not much
> soil, and immediately they sprang up, since they
> had no depth of soil, but when the sun rose they
> were scorched; and since they had no root they
> withered away. Other seeds fell upon thorns,
> and the thorns grew up and choked them.
> Other seeds fell on good soil and brought forth
> grain, some a hundredfold, some sixty, some
> thirty. He who has ears, let him hear."
>
> —Matthew 13:1-9

By this parable he was trying to tell them it would not
be easy to win people to the kingdom. But they, the disciples, were to keep on patiently telling the good news
over and over again. There would always be some who
would listen and believe. They were to plant the seed
of the truth about God. Somewhere, sometime it would
find good soil, and take root in the hearts of people.
Long years afterward the disciples were to remember and
take heart whenever they became discouraged.

As Jesus' fame as a teacher and miracle worker began
to spread across the country, the religious leaders at Jerusalem became interested in him. At first they had paid

little attention to him, for there were many wandering preachers in those days and they thought he was just another one of these. But when they heard what great crowds of people he was attracting, they sent out some of their members to hear him.

At first these delegates from Jerusalem, who were mostly Pharisees, liked what they heard. Jesus seemed to be teaching about the same thing that they were. He was telling people that they must give up their evil ways and live according to the rule of God. The Pharisees had long taught that people should live by God's law, only they thought that living by God's law meant to be careful in all outward things, such as saying prayers in public regularly, doing no work on the sabbath day, eating no pork or other unclean foods, and being sure to wash one's hands after touching a Gentile. They did not see as yet that Jesus was talking about a different kind of religion, one that changed the hearts of men from selfishness to kindness and from hate to love. Neither did they understand what Jesus meant by "the kingdom of God," but even his disciples did not understand this as yet.

One of the Pharisees, a man by the name of Nicodemus (nik-o-dee'mus), became so interested that he called on Jesus late at night so that he could have a private talk with him after the crowds had gone home. The two talked for hours even though Jesus was tired from a day of almost constant speaking and teaching. He sensed that Nicodemus was a good man and the kind who would make a great disciple if he could only win him.

Jesus told him about the kingdom of God which was based on love rather than law and tried to explain to him how much God loved his children and how God wanted his children to love him in return.

The words struck deep into the heart of Nicodemus. He had long felt that God was more loving than his

73

fellow Pharisees thought him to be. How wonderful it would be to believe in a God like that. It was what he wanted to believe but all his life he had been taught that God was stern and demanding, that one must obey the law to the letter or God would grow angry with him. How sweet it would be to believe that God loved him as a good father loves his child. Nicodemus thought of his own children and how much he loved them. They meant more than his own life to him. Did God love him like that? It was all too wonderful to believe.

Jesus sensed what was going on in Nicodemus' mind and said to him,

> "Truly, truly, I say to you, unless one is born
> anew, he cannot see the kingdom of God."
> —John 3:3

Nicodemus' eyes opened wide. What was Jesus saying? Could he be born all over again? Could he start life again with a fresh, new mind, believing from childhood that God was loving and gracious? It was too much for his mind to get hold of all at once and he asked,

> "How can a man be born when he is old?
> Can he enter a second time into his mother's
> womb and be born?"
> —John 3:4

His mind was so full he hardly knew what he was asking. But Jesus did not laugh at him. He only said gently,

> "Truly, truly, I say to you, unless one is born
> of water and the Spirit, he cannot enter the
> kingdom of God."
> —John 3:5

◄ Irrigation of crops dates back to biblical times. Here two Jews on the shore of the Sea of Galilee apply the same methods of irrigation that were used during Jesus' time. This method is still in general use today. *Photo by Black Star*

Then Jesus went on to explain that this was a spiritual birth he was talking about. It was an unseen change on the inside of a man that gave him a new mind and heart. It was like the wind, he went on to say, a man could feel it and hear it but he could not see it.

It was nearly daylight when Nicodemus left and even then he found it hard to go. He wanted so much to believe what Jesus said but it was all so new and different and it was hard for a man like him to accept it. He must have time to make up his mind. He had to be sure.

Jesus watched him walk slowly away and he looked after him with longing in his eyes. How close Nicodemus was to the kingdom and yet how far away. Jesus wished that he might have told him openly, "I am the one whom God has sent to tell you all this." He knew he dare not do so, for that was something Nicodemus, and everyone else, must discover for himself. So Jesus turned back to his disciples who had long ago wrapped themselves in their coats and gone to sleep.

Not all the Pharisees were like Nicodemus. Others among them became jealous of Jesus. Many of the Pharisees were also rabbis and they soon discovered that their students were leaving their classes and going to hear Jesus. They did not like this and began to watch for something they could find fault with in Jesus' conduct. They were not long finding it.

Matthew, shortly after he was called to be one of the disciples, gave a dinner in honor of Jesus and invited all his old friends so that they might meet and hear him. Now Matthew had been a tax collector for the Roman government and several of his tax-collector friends came to the dinner. Of all the people the Pharisees hated, they hated most of all the tax collectors. Many of them were dishonest and the Pharisees felt that all of them were terrible sinners.

A committee of the Pharisees lost no time in coming to some of the disciples to find fault with Jesus. They said to the disciples, "Why does your teacher eat with tax collectors and sinners?

The disciples did not know what to answer but when Jesus heard it he laughed a little and said,

> "Those who are well have no need of a physician, but those who are sick . . . I came not to call the righteous, but sinners."
>
> —Matthew 9:12-13

A few days later a more serious thing happened. It was near the close of the sabbath. It had been a busy day of teaching for Jesus and his disciples. There had not been time to stop for lunch. Now, late in the day they were on their way to their camp and they were all hungry. Growing along the path was some wheat a kindly farmer had left there for hungry travelers to eat. The disciples knew they were welcome to it, so they plucked off some of the heads of the wheat, rolled them in their hands to make the grains pop out and then ate them.

Some Pharisees saw them and they made a great issue of the matter. It was all right for the disciples to eat the grain but to pluck off the heads and roll them in their hands, that was harvesting and harvesting was work. Therefore, they were guilty of working on the sabbath, a thing for which they could be arrested.

Again Jesus laughed about the matter, for it seemed so foolish to him. But it made him sad, too. The opposition was beginning. Not only would he be unable to win many of the Pharisees to him, most of them were rapidly becoming his enemies.

Other groups in the government at Jerusalem also began to take note of Jesus and sought to find out just what kind of teacher he was. The lawyers were sure that this bold, young man from Galilee could not know anything about the Law. They thought it would be fun to ask him a tricky question and show up his ignorance of the Law before the people.

Now one of the difficult questions of the day was, Who is one's neighbor? The Torah taught that one should love his neighbor but it did not say who was one's neighbor. The lawyers had a dozen different answers to the question, so whatever Jesus answered would be wrong and before they got through with him, they thought, they would have him confused so that they could trap him. They would show the crowd that this Jesus was just an ignorant fellow from the country.

The lawyers chose one of their number as a spokesman and started out in great glee to meet Jesus. They found him out on the rugged mountain road that ran from Jerusalem to Jericho.

When the lawyers saw Jesus, their spokesman began to ask him questions and he walked right into the trap just as they had hoped he would. The spokesman had asked,

> "Teacher, what shall I do to inherit eternal life?" He (Jesus) said to him, "What is written in the law? How do you read?" And he answered, "You shall love the Lord your God with all your heart, and with all your soul, and with all your strength, and with all your mind; and your neighbor as yourself." And he said to him, "You have answered right; do this, and you will live."
>
> —Luke 10:25-28

The lawyer could not help smiling a little. Every-

78

thing was going just as they had planned. Now the spokesman for the lawyers was ready to spring the trap and he cried out in a loud voice so everyone could hear, "And who is my neighbor?" (Luke 10:29.)

Jesus did not answer for a moment; then he began to tell a story, a story so rich in meaning and so beautiful in thought it will live as long as the earth lasts.

> "A man was going down from Jerusalem to Jericho, and he fell among robbers, who stripped him and beat him, and departed, leaving him half-dead. Now by chance a priest was going down that road; and when he saw him he passed by on the other side. So likewise a Levite, when he came to the place and saw him, passed by on the other side. But a Samaritan, as he journeyed, came to where he was; and when he saw him, he had compassion, and went to him and bound up his wounds, pouring on oil and wine; then he set him on his own beast and brought him to an inn, and took care of him. And the next day he took out two denarii and gave them to the innkeeper, saying, 'Take care of him; and whatever more you spend, I will repay you when I come back.' "
>
> —Luke 10:30-35

The smiling lawyers grew quiet as the story was told. Here was an answer they had never thought of and one about which they had no argument.

When the story was finished and they had nothing to say, Jesus turned to them and said,

> "Which of these three, do you think, proved neighbor to the man who fell among the robbers?"
>
> —Luke 10:36

79

The spokesman answered softly and humbly, "The one who showed mercy on him." (Luke 10:37.)

Then Jesus touched him gently on the shoulder, smiled in a kindly way and said, "Go and do likewise." Slowly the spokesman and his lawyer friends turned and walked back toward Jerusalem. Jesus watched them sadly. They, too, had come very near to the kingdom but they would not enter in. Would they also turn and become his enemies?

A few weeks later something else happened that had to be taken very seriously. This time the opposition was in deadly earnest and Jesus knew that real danger was at hand.

Jesus and his disciples had gone, as their custom was, to worship in a synagogue on the sabbath. A number of Pharisees were present. A man with a deformed hand came to Jesus asking for healing. The Pharisees at once raised the question, "Is it lawful to heal on the sabbath?" (Matthew 12:10.)

Jesus knew they had not asked for information but only to find fault with him. They did not want to know the truth, they only wanted to prove themselves right. He tried to reason with them,

> "What man of you, if he has one sheep and it
> falls into a pit on the sabbath, will not lay hold
> of it and lift it out? Of how much more value
> is a man than a sheep!"

> —Matthew 12:11-12

◄ As Jesus walked from one town to another, he often spent the time teaching his disciples.

The Pharisees had no answer for this. They just sat and sneered. Jesus knew that these small-minded men had no love in their hearts for their fellow men. They would rescue a sheep on the sabbath for it was worth money, but a fellow man in suffering did not move them at all. Anger flamed in Jesus at the hardness of their hearts. He could not let such lack of love go unchallenged.

"Stretch out your hand," he commanded the man with the deformed hand, and as he did it was made well. The people shouted with joy, then turned on the Pharisees and laughed them out of the synagogue. This only made the proud Pharisees angrier than ever. They had been made to look foolish in the eyes of the people, but they would get even. They would destroy Jesus one way or another. That night they called a meeting of their friends and began to make plans as to how they were to do it. The lion of opposition was beginning to roar.

The Seeds

The seeds and the hand of the sower on the first page of this chapter recall what Jesus said about the ways in which his messages are received. Although Jesus' words in Matthew 13:3-23 are called the Parable of the Sower, really they tell a parable of different kinds of soil. What kind of "soil" are you providing for Jesus' message?

7.

The Sea and the Wind

A FEW OF THE PEOPLE became Jesus' enemies, but they were only the few. Most of the
people were friendly to him and were glad to
hear him even though they did not take him
seriously or believe deeply in what he taught.
Here and there he continued to find some who
did believe deeply. In the village of Bethany,
a few miles from Jerusalem, he found three
persons who did believe. They were two sisters, Mary and Martha, and their brother,
Lazarus (Lăz'a-rus). They had a large house
where they invited Jesus and the disciples to
stay whenever they were teaching nearby.

Of the three, Mary was the most interested and Jesus knew that before long she would come to believe fully in the kingdom. He wished that he might spend long hours with her, Martha, and Lazarus. But after the Pharisees began to plot against him, he realized it would be dangerous to remain near Jerusalem, so, saying farewell to his friends at Bethany, he and his disciples set out for Galilee.

On the way north they passed through Samaria. They came to the town of Sychar and while the disciples went into town to buy food, Jesus rested at the town well at the edge of the city. As he was resting a woman came to draw water and Jesus asked her for a drink. The woman was surprised, for men seldom spoke to women in public in those days and more than that Jesus was a Jew and few of them would speak to a Samaritan. She asked,

> "How is it that you, a Jew, ask a drink of me, a woman of Samaria?" . . . Jesus answered her, "If you knew the gift of God, and who it is that is saying to you, 'Give me a drink,' you would have asked him, and he would have given you living water . . . Every one who drinks of this water will thirst again, but whoever drinks of the water that I shall give him will never thirst; the water that I shall give him will become in him a spring of water welling up to eternal life."

> —John 4:9-10, 13-14

The woman was quick to see that Jesus was a man of God so she put to him a question that Jews and Samaritans often argued about and sometimes fought over. The Jews had their temple at Jerusalem and they said that was the proper place to worship God. The Samaritans had a smaller temple on Mt. Gerizim near the city of

Samaria and they held that this was the proper place to worship.

Jesus answered her by saying that the place where one worships God does not matter but only the spirit in which one worships. He said:

> "Woman, believe me, the hour is coming when neither on this mountain nor in Jerusalem will you worship the Father . . . The true worshipers will worship the Father in spirit and truth, for such the Father seeks to worship him. God is spirit, and those who worship him must worship him in spirit and truth."
>
> —John 4:21, 23-24

The woman thought this the best answer to the problem she had ever heard and she ran into town to tell everyone that there was a man of God out at the well. Soon a crowd gathered. Jesus and the disciples taught them about the kingdom and made many friends there.

After stopping at other villages in Samaria, Jesus and his disciples made their way back to Capernaum. Peter, Andrew, James, and John lost no time getting down to the shore of the Sea of Galilee and there tied to a pier was their beloved boat. Zebedee, the father of James and John, had taken good care of it, and it was clean and bright. Getting in they took a sail out into the lake. Never did men handle a boat more lovingly. They ran their hands over her planks and each took a turn at the tiller to get the feel of her in the wind. They shouted and laughed and sang their old fisherman songs. It was nearly dark when they returned to shore and carefully folded the sails away. How they had missed the boat and the sea while they had been with Jesus in the dry, dusty country around Jerusalem!

Next day Jesus also came down to the beach and a

great crowd of people gathered to hear him speak. There were so many of them that they kept pushing down the beach until Jesus was almost in the water. He motioned to Peter, who untied his boat and brought it close to shore so Jesus could get aboard and speak from the boat.

As Peter held the boat steady with an oar stuck into the sand and listened to Jesus tell parable after parable to the crowd, he thought of all the strange adventures he had been upon in this boat. He remembered the proud day they had launched her and marked the way she sat true in the water. He thought of the dark nights he had fished from her and of the storms he had weathered in her. But no adventure had been more thrilling than this. The great voice of Jesus was rolling like music out to the farthest edges of the crowd. The people leaned forward as they listened as if they could not wait for the next word to reach them. Peter felt as if the very sky were listening to what was being said from his boat and never had he been more proud of her.

For some time Jesus and his disciples made their headquarters at Capernaum, teaching in the city, out along the lake and in many towns nearby. Some of the Pharisees from Jerusalem came to spy on them. They had heard about Jesus' miracles and they demanded that he perform one for them. But Jesus refused. He knew that if they would not believe his words, they would not believe in a miracle, for they did not want to believe. So he said to them, " 'No sign shall be given . . . except the sign of Jonah.' " (Matthew 16:4.) It was a strange

The opposition begins. Those in the temple began to see that➤ their priestly positions were being threatened by the teachings of this man from Nazareth.

saying and even the disciples wondered at it. They knew the story of Jonah who had been for three days in the stomach of a great fish and then was cast out to live again. What could Jesus mean by the sign of Jonah?

Not only did the Pharisees make trouble for Jesus, the friendly Galileans also were causing him concern. Some of them were openly talking about him as their Messiah who would soon raise an army and drive out the hated Romans. The situation worried Jesus. He needed to make clear to his disciples that the kingdom of God was not made up of armies and swords. But there was never time enough and even when he did manage to speak to the disciples alone, they did not understand him. They, too, wanted him to become an earthly king and some among them were already dreaming of the things they would do when they, as his helpers, were in control of the government. They even fell to quarreling about who would get the most important offices when their Master became king. Peter, James, and John were sure they would get the best offices, while Judas and some of his friends were sure they would get them. The quarrels became so bitter at times the disciples would hardly speak to one another.

Meanwhile word came that John the Baptist had been killed by Herod Antipas, governor of Galilee. The news brought fear and sorrow to the disciples. They had known and loved John. In fact, Nathanael and one or two others had at one time been disciples of John. If the governor could kill John, he might also try to destroy Jesus. This made them more anxious than ever for Jesus to set up his kingdom and raise an army to protect himself.

Jesus knew it was time he had a frank talk with them about the matter. He must take them away from the crowds where he could teach them carefully and patiently about the true kingdom of God. So he asked

Peter to get his boat ready, and early one morning they set out across the lake for the desert country on the opposite side.

The boat was heavily loaded with 13 men aboard and a basket of food that Judas had brought along for their noonday meal. It was a bright, clear morning with a good wind to fill the sails, and Peter proudly landed his boat on the opposite shore in less than an hour.

Going up on a little hill above the lake, Jesus sat down with his disciples and all morning long they discussed the meaning of the kingdom. For once the disciples seemed to be getting the idea of what he meant. He could see light beginning to break in the face of Peter. Even Judas listened quietly and seemed to be thinking deeply.

At noon they ate a lunch of bread and dried fruits. The cool, clear air made them hungry and they ate everything Judas had brought along. They had just finished eating when they heard the sound of voices down along the lake. A great crowd of people, learning where Jesus was, had walked all the way around the south end of the lake. Having sighted Peter's boat, the younger ones were running ahead and crying back to the others, "Here they are! Here they are!"

Jesus was deeply moved by what they had done. It was a long, hard walk around the lake and must have taken them several hours but they wanted to hear and see him so much that they had been willing to come all this way. He could not be angry at them for breaking in on his meeting with the disciples.

Leading the crowd up into a place between two hills where all could be seated, Jesus began to teach them many things in parables. He used story after story to show them what he meant by the kingdom of God.[1] All afternoon the crowd listened quietly to him though now

[1]Examples of these parables may be found in Matthew 13 and Luke 13.

and then groups of young men would gather at the edge of the crowd and seem to be talking over something between themselves.

Late afternoon came and Jesus knew it was time the people were starting their long tramp back home. He stopped speaking to them but they cried out for "just one more story" and refused to leave. He knew most of them had brought little or no lunch with them and they would be faint from hunger before they could get to their homes for supper. He wished he might give them something to eat. He called in his disciples to discuss the matter with them. Where could they get food enough to feed all these people? No towns were near but perhaps the boat could make a fast run across the lake and bring back something.

The disciples raised an objection at once. It would cost a lot of money to feed all these people and though there was plenty in the treasury, they did not want to spend it for a picnic supper.

"Why," they exclaimed, "it would take 200 denarii[2] to buy even a little food for all these people!"

A boy about 12 years of age was standing nearby and heard the disciples talking. He had a package wrapped in a napkin under his arm. This he laid in a disciple's hands without saying a word and the disciple, not knowing what else to do, slowly unwrapped it. In it were five small, hard biscuits and two fish. He sneered when he saw what it was and was about to throw it away when Jesus, who had been watching, took the package in one of his hands. Then he looked at the boy and laid his other hand on his shoulder. How he loved this boy who, though he had so little to give, gave it so willingly and

---

[2] A denarius (de-nar′i-us) was worth about 20 cents but was as much as a man could earn in a day. Two hundred denarii would represent more than $1,000 in our money today.

eagerly. Would he dare show the crowd what God could do with gifts like this?

Suddenly his head went back and he lifted his eyes upward in prayer. Then he broke the bread and fish into little pieces and began to hand them to the disciples. The startled disciples stood in silence not knowing what to do. The crowd sensed that something wonderful was happening and became deathly still. No one moved. It was all like a picture—the tall figure of Jesus standing beside a boy whose face was lifted toward him, the disciples holding pieces of bread and fish.

Finally someone broke the stillness and came running with a basket. Other baskets soon appeared and these the disciples filled and began to pass among the people. Not until everyone had been served did anyone speak, then, as if by a signal, everyone began to talk all at once. Never had such a thing as this happened, a tiny lunch made into enough food for hundreds of people. Afterward, when they tried to tell other people about it, they could not be sure what had happened. They were sure only that for a few minutes they had seemed to stand at the edge of a world where the presence of God was very real.

When all had eaten their fill and the wonder of the hour had passed, the young men in the crowd began to gather into groups. Suddenly a shout arose from one group. Another took it up, then another. Now they were marching with the various groups falling in behind one another. Some produced long knives that they had kept hidden until now beneath their coats. Others picked up sticks and stones. They were poor weapons but it made them feel more like soldiers. With courage growing they began to march. They were out of step, their lines were crooked, and their poor clothing did not look much like uniforms but even so, they had become an army. They had found a leader whom they would gladly follow

91

unto death. If Jesus would not choose them, then they would choose him. They would force him to become their Messiah. With him as their leader they would drive out the Romans and their country should be free once more. With a leader as strong and kingly as Jesus who could feed his army from practically nothing as he had fed the crowd that day, they could not only defeat the Romans, they could conquer all nations and make Jerusalem the capital of the world.

This idea swept like wildfire not only through the groups of young men but all through the crowd of people who now were shouting and cheering the ragged army. There was confusion and noise everywhere. Still the young soldiers marched.

Suddenly the marching men stopped. Where was Jesus? A little while ago he had been standing there, his tall figure towering above the crowd. Now he was nowhere to be seen. A search was made of the crowd but he was not there. Bands of men set out in all directions. They searched the hills and the beach until long after dark but nowhere could they find Jesus.

It was late when the search was given up and the young army broke up, each man to find his way home as best he could. Without a king they were no longer an army.

The Fish and Loaves

The symbol of the fish and bread at the beginning of this chapter represent the feeding of the 5,000. (Matthew 14:15-21.)

8.

Light on the Mountain

TIRED AS THEY WERE, Jesus ordered his disciples to gather up their things and prepare for a long journey. Before long they were on their way out of Capernaum and they did not stop until after daylight when they made camp in a wooded place well back off the road. Here they rested throughout the day and took to the road again at night. For four nights they traveled rapidly northward until they were out of the state of Galilee and in the foreign country of Caesarea Philippi (sē′za-rē′a fi-lip′ī).

Jesus did not like to drive his men like this

but he knew he must, for the work was in danger. At Jerusalem he had been forced to flee from his enemies who might kill him before his work was done. In Galilee it was his friends who were endangering the work he must do. They had tried to make of him the kind of king he could never be, and he knew it would be impossible to get the idea out of their heads, at least for a while. His disciples did not understand as yet the meaning of the kingdom of God he had come to establish. He knew he must get them away into a place where they were unknown so that he could spend time alone with them helping them to see that the kingdom he had come to set up was one of peace, good will, and obedience to the will of God. It was a kingdom that would live in the hearts of men. It could not be set up by the power of an army nor defended with a sword. It must begin in the hearts of his disciples and spread through the power of love and truth to the hearts of other persons whom they should win to it. These, in turn, would win others and in this way his kingdom would spread slowly around the whole world.

The winter months were now at hand, so Jesus and his disciples rented rooms in Caesarea Philippi. Finally, the day came when he put them to the test to see if they knew who he really was. "Who do men say that I am?" he asked. (Mark 8:27.)

A lively discussion followed with the disciples reporting what they had heard the people say about him. They thought he was one of the great prophets returned to life such as Elijah (ē-lī'ja) who was one of the first prophets. Others thought he might be another John the Baptist. Judas and Simon the Zealot still held to the idea that he was another David who should rule as king over the world. Through all this discussion Peter had remained silent, though he usually talked so much that Jesus would have to stop him so the others could have a chance.

When the discussion had gone on for awhile, Jesus

94

turned to them and said, "Who do you say that I am?" (Mark 8:29.)

Then Peter did a strange thing for him—big, strong, fellow that he was. He stood up and looked at Jesus for a long time with tears slowly forming in his eyes. Then he fell to his knees and bowed his head to the floor. Lifting his head a little, he said in a whisper, "You are the Christ." (Mark 8:29.) It was all he could say but it was enough.

Peter's whispered words went through the group of disciples like an electric shock. One by one they looked at Jesus and suddenly saw him through new eyes. They felt a little ashamed that they had not seen it before, for it had been there for them to see all along. One by one they fell to their knees, some whispering, some shouting, "You are the Christ!" Only Judas remained seated; he seemed to be thinking deeply.

Jesus looked upon him and longed to help him see more clearly. He was a strong man who might do either great good or great harm. Jesus marked him for special attention in the days to come but right now he must respond to the others. This was the hour he had been working for, and it was a happy one indeed. All but one of his disciples had come to see that he was the Son of God. Now they could understand why he could not be their kind of king, for as God's Son he must be loyal only to God's will and establish the kind of kingdom God wanted.

Commanding Peter to rise, Jesus spoke to him using, at first, the old name he had worn in his fisherman days:

"Blessed are you, Simon Bar-Jona! For flesh and blood has not revealed this to you, but my Father who is in heaven. And I tell you, you are Peter, and on this rock I will build my church, and the powers of death shall not prevail against it."

—Matthew 16:17-18

By this Jesus meant that belief in him as the Son of God would be the "rock" upon which the church was to be built. True to this teaching of Jesus, most churches today require a person wishing to become a Christian to make the same statement Peter made.

A few days after this Jesus took Peter, John, and James on a short trip out into the mountains. In the crisp winter air they talked earnestly about the kingdom and then knelt to pray. As they were praying, a change seemed to come over Jesus. His face and clothes seemed as if they were made of light and a voice came out of a cloud saying, "This is my beloved Son; listen to him." The disciples did not understand what the vision and the voice meant, but Jesus did.

Once again God had spoken as he had done at the time of his baptism, and Jesus knew it was God's sign that he was pleased with his work. It meant that the training he had given the disciples would do. The rest they could learn as they went along. Jesus knew they might make mistakes, might even prove unfaithful at times, but that, in the long run, they would not fail.

Deep in his heart he knew the voice meant that God had something more for him to do and at first he did not like to think about it. It seemed almost too much for God to ask of him. Yet he knew it must be done. Up until now he had fled from his enemies so that he could remain alive and teach his disciples. That work was done. Now he must face his enemies. It was clearly God's will and, much as he wanted to live, he wanted more to do God's will.

He knew he must go back to Jerusalem regardless of the danger that awaited him there. Even if his enemies should kill him, he was sure God would use his death in some way. He knew God was stronger than death and that he need not fear it.

Jesus frequently went off by himself to meditate and pray. These moments with God gave him strength to meet the opposition that was rapidly growing.

From that time Jesus began to show his disciples that he must go to Jerusalem and suffer many things from the elders and chief priests and scribes, and be killed, and on the third day be raised. And Peter took him and began to rebuke him, saying, "God forbid, Lord! This shall never happen to you." But he turned and said to Peter, "Get behind me, Satan! You are a hindrance to me; for you are not on the side of God, but of men."

—Matthew 16:21-23

Jesus also saw that not only must he be willing to give up his life for the kingdom, his disciples must be willing to make the same sacrifice. So he said to them:

"If any man would come after me, let him deny himself and take up his cross and follow me. For whoever would save his life will lose it, and whoever loses his life for my sake will find it. For what will it profit a man, if he gains the whole world and forfeits his life? Or what shall a man give in return for his life?"

—Matthew 16:24-26

The winter was now nearly over and good traveling days were ahead. In a few days Jesus and the disciples left Caesarea Philippi and started back toward Capernaum and the Sea of Galilee.

When they arrived back at Capernaum, more helpers were added to the disciple band making their number now 70 in all. These Jesus organized into teams of two and sent them out to speak in the villages round about. Some he sent on into Samaria to arrange a speaking tour for him through that country. They were to tell the people he was coming, for he knew this would be his last trip and he wanted to speak to as many people as possible.

Throughout the spring months he was constantly on the move, spending a day in this village and another in that one. Crowds of people came to hear him but they were not as large as they once were, for he was speaking plainly about the kingdom and many felt his teachings were too hard for them. He told them frankly that the kingdom was not easy to enter, that they must be willing to make great sacrifices, even to risking their lives for it.

On several occasions young men came and said they wanted to become his disciples. Jesus always welcomed these but he also warned them of what it would cost them to follow him.

One young man who came was a scribe. In those days there were no printing presses and all books and legal papers had to be copied by hand. Persons who did this kind of work were known as scribes. This man said "Teacher, I will follow you wherever you go." (Matthew 8:19.)

Jesus had a long talk with him for he thought he might become a disciple. But he soon discovered that the young man wanted only an easy job. Copying books was hard work and he had seen the disciples going about from village to village. They had good clothes and the villagers often fed them or gave them money. This looked like easy work to the scribe. He did not know about the long hours of study, the marches in the night in order to be at the next village to teach all day, nor the complete devotion required of disciples.

After talking to the scribe, Jesus said:

"Foxes have holes, and birds of the air have nests; but the Son of man has nowhere to lay his head."
—Matthew 8:20

99

This surprised the scribe for he had thought of Jesus as having everything. When he discovered that Jesus had only enough money to buy bread and did not have even a home of his own, he decided being his disciple was not easy and he turned away.

Another man came to Jesus. He, too, wanted to be a disciple, but he knew his father would not like it. He said, "Lord, let me first go and bury my father." (Matthew 8:21.) By this he meant that he would remain at home as long as his father lived. When his father had died, he would be free to follow Jesus.

Jesus answered him, "Follow me, and leave the dead to bury their own dead." (Matthew 8:22.) This sounded like a hard saying to many, but Peter knew why it was necessary. He had left his wife and it was not easy for her. But she was willing to make the sacrifice. James and John understood for they had left their father to carry on his fishing business as best he could without their help. They, too, loved their father and would liked to have remained with him. But they loved the kingdom of God more.

Down through Samaria went Jesus and the disciples, teaching, preaching, healing. They crossed the Jordan River and preached for a while on the east side of it. Whenever they found anyone who showed a deep interest in the things of the kingdom, they would invite this person to join a small group where the matter could be discussed and questions answered.

The people pressed upon him from everywhere, particularly the children. They had loved his stories and now they wanted to touch him. They crowded in among the grownups who were all trying to talk to Jesus at the same time. Judas and some of the other disciples started to push the children away. When Jesus saw what they were doing, he scolded the disciples gently, then taking two of the smaller children up in his arms, he called out to

And they were bringing children to him, that he might touch
them. . . . And he took them in his arms and blessed them,
laying his hands upon them. (Mark 10:13, 16.)

the crowd for silence. When they had grown quiet enough to hear, he said:

"Let the children come to me, do not hinder them; for to such belongs the kingdom of God. Truly, I say to you, whoever does not receive the kingdom of God like a child shall not enter it." And he took them in his arms and blessed them, laying his hands upon them.

—Mark 10:14-16

Jesus and his disciples crossed back over the river and came to Jericho. Here a funny thing happened. A fairly large crowd had gathered to hear Jesus. There was in the crowd a very short man by the name of Zacchaeus (za-kē'us). In order to see he climbed up in a sycamore tree. It was a funny sight, the man sitting up there on a limb like an owl. The people began to laugh but the little man just laughed with them, for he had a happy spirit.

When Jesus saw it, he laughed too and called out merrily, "Zacchaeus, make haste and come down; for I must stay at your house today." (Luke 19:5.)

Zacchaeus lost no time getting down out of the tree, for a great honor had come to him. Many people in that crowd would have liked to have had Jesus go home with them. Some did not like it that Zacchaeus had been chosen since he worked for the Roman government as a despised tax collector. Jesus knew he had found a man who was ready and willing to believe in the kingdom.

Zacchaeus was willing to make any sacrifice for the sake of the kingdom. He had made money, but money had not brought him a rich life. He saw that Jesus' teachings would and opened his heart to them. As Jesus was leaving, Zacchaeus announced that he would give away half of his wealth to the poor and that he would give back four times over any money that he had taken wrongfully

102

from anyone. Zacchaeus would no longer be rich with money when this was done but he would be rich in life.

Jesus looked upon him lovingly and said, "Today salvation has come to this house . . . For the Son of man came to seek and to save the lost." (Luke 19:9, 10.)

Many things happened on the trip that were not funny. Spies from Jerusalem were in the crowds that listened to him almost every day. Sometimes they tried to argue with him and they often tried to break up his meetings by shouting and making loud noises. Jesus knew that they were watching for an opportunity to turn the people against him. Let him make one little slip and they would pounce on him like a pack of wolves. So far, their heckling and troublemaking had only drawn the people closer to Jesus. Time and again the people would have turned on the spies and beaten them had he encouraged them to do so. But he knew the kingdom of God was a way of peace, not a way of fighting. So he bore with the spies.

Meanwhile some of the Pharisees at Jerusalem had come to despise Jesus so much that they made friends with a group known as the Herodians (he-rod'e-ans) a party that was on the side of the wicked king, Herod, and his family. The first Herod died while Jesus was a young boy but his children still ruled under the Roman government. It was one of these, Herod Antipas, governor of Galilee, who had killed John the Baptist.

Ordinarily the Pharisees would have nothing to do with the Herodians but in their blind hatred of Jesus they were willing to work with anyone who would help them destroy Jesus.

Together the two groups planned a plot that they were sure would turn the people against Jesus and might even send him to jail. Of all the things the Jewish people disliked about the Roman government, they disliked most the paying of taxes to that government. Jesus had been the friend of tax collectors such as Matthew and Zacchaeus. If they could show that he was a friend of the Romans and was in favor of Roman taxes, the people would turn against him. Or if they could show that he was against Roman taxes, they could make a charge against him to the Roman government and have him arrested as a dangerous enemy of the government.

They held a long meeting and came up with a trick question, from which, they were sure, Jesus could not escape. The lawyers might have failed to trap Jesus with their question, but there would be no way for him to get out of this. The lawyers had asked their question more or less in fun but these people were in deadly earnest. They would not be content to make a fool of Jesus. They were out to destroy his influence, even if this meant prison or death.

The question they had made up was this, Is it right to pay taxes to Caesar, emperor of Rome? Whichever way Jesus answered it, he would be in trouble, either with the people or the Romans.

The Pharisees selected some of their group to be their spokesmen, just as the lawyers had done, and these approached Jesus as he was teaching near Jericho. They made a great show of being friendly to him so they could catch him off guard. They began by praising him as a great and honest teacher:

> "Teacher, we know that you are true, and care for no man; for you do not regard the position of men, but truly teach the way of God."

> —Mark 12:14

They said this with a smile on their faces. Jesus was not deceived. He could see the mockery back of the smiles. The Pharisees were sure they had Jesus right where they wanted him and they cried out their trick question loudly so everyone around about would be sure to hear it.

104

"Is it lawful to pay taxes to Caesar, or not?" one of them shouted. Just to be sure Jesus could not get out of the trap, another shouted, "Should we pay them, or should we not?"

Jesus realized he was on the spot. How should he answer? Was this the moment when he was to face arrest and possibly death? He lifted his head in a moment of prayer and listening, as once he had on a road in Galilee. In a moment he knew how God wanted him to handle the situation.

"Bring me a coin, and let me look at it," he said quietly. Someone in the crowd quickly produced a Roman coin. He turned it over and over in his hand, then holding it up he pointed to the side that had Caesar's head on it.

"Whose likeness and whose name is here?" he asked of the spokesmen.

"Caesar's," they answered, not realizing that they were the ones who had walked into a trap.

"Very well," said Jesus, "Render to Caesar the things that are Caesar's, and to God the things that are God's." He had escaped their trap with an answer of good sense. They were to pay their taxes to Rome, but first of all and above all they were to give their hearts and their loyalty to God.

A few years later, followers of Jesus were to remember this statement. When the Roman government began to oppose the Christian religion, the Christians obeyed the laws of the government as long as they could. But when a law was made forbidding them to follow Christ, they bravely proclaimed their faith even at the risk of their lives.

The Pharisees, who had come to spy on Jesus, realized that he had escaped their trap. They turned away, but now they were determined to destroy this troublesome

105

teacher. Jesus was well aware that this would not be the last he would hear from them. The disciples also understood that the Pharisees were not through. In Jerusalem these men had considerable influence and could easily stir up trouble for Jesus. So the disciples pleaded with him to turn back to Galilee, but he insisted on continuing up to Jerusalem.

Up the Jericho road toward Jerusalem went Jesus and his disciples; up the crooked, narrow road, up past the caves and the deep canyons, up to the turn in the road where the city could be seen bright and shining in the springtime sun.

When he saw the city, Jesus stopped and looked at it for a long time. How lovely it looked from the mountainside! If only the people would listen to his message, if only they would believe and change their way of life, the city could be as beautiful as it looked from a distance. Tears came to his eyes, for he still loved Jerusalem as he had when he had first seen it as a boy. From the depths of his heart, he cried:

"O Jerusalem, Jerusalem, killing the prophets and stoning those who are sent to you! How often would I have gathered your children together as a hen gathers her brood under her wings, and you would not!"

—Matthew 23:37

The Sun

The symbol of the sun at the beginning of this chapter was frequently used by Jesus to explain the good way of life. In Matthew 13:43 he said, "Then the righteous will shine like the sun in the kingdom of their Father." In John 8:12 Jesus said, "I am the light of the world; he who follows me will not walk in darkness, but will have the light of life."

106

9.

King for a Day

IT WAS THE PASSOVER season and once more great crowds of Jews had come from all over the known world to celebrate the occasion at Jerusalem. Every house in the city was full of guests and thousands more were camped on the hills outside the city. Jesus and his disciples made camp in an olive grove some two or three miles from the city. Here they spent the sabbath day, the last one they were ever to have together as teacher and disciples.

Early the next morning, which would be Sunday on the calendars of today, Jesus and his disciples set out for the temple where he had planned to teach throughout the day. They had gone only a little way when a crowd of pilgrims began to gather about them. Someone began to sing a well-known and much-loved song,

> "Hosanna to the Son of David! Blessed be he who comes in the name of the Lord! Hosanna in the highest!"
>
> —Matthew 21:9

Quickly the song was taken up by others and once again the crowd was like an army, an army that had found its king.

This time Jesus did not try to stop them. He was their king, though a different kind from what they thought him to be. He would use the occasion to show them the kind of king he really was.

While he spoke to the crowd about the kingdom of God as a realm of love in the hearts of men, he sent his disciples in search of a donkey on which he would ride at the head of the procession. It was another way he would use to show what kind of king he was. Any other king would have asked for a chariot drawn by horses, but he would ride on a lowly donkey, humbly yet kingly. He would also call the mind of the people to an ancient prophecy:

> "Behold, your king is coming to you, humble, and mounted on an ass, and on a colt, the foal of an ass."
>
> —Matthew 21:5

Soon the disciples returned with a small donkey, one that was just barely old enough to be ridden. They put their coats on the donkey and Jesus sat on these, his long legs almost dragging the ground.

Down the road went the little donkey. It was a heavy load for his young back but he bore it proudly. He seemed to know something great was happening. More and more persons joined the procession as it moved toward Jerusalem. Louder and louder grew the song. Some persons ran ahead and laid their coats in the road to make the path smooth for the donkey on which Jesus rode. Others gathered flowers and branches to lay in the path of the procession.

It was a beautiful sight in the bright morning sun, with the brightly colored coats and flowers along the path. Shouts and songs of the people echoed among the hills while the stately figure of Jesus sat astride the back of the little donkey. The procession grew in number as it moved down through the valley that separated the city of Jerusalem from the olive grove, then slowly climbed toward the gate of the city.

As the procession neared the gate, the gatekeepers stood aside to let it pass. They had orders not to let a mob enter the city but this great crowd did not seem like a mob. It was made up of men, women and children, singing psalms and hymns and following a kindly looking person on a harmless donkey. They waved palm branches in the air, but carried no swords. Through the gate the crowd poured into the narrow, winding streets of the city, pushing all other traffic out of the way. Up toward the temple it moved and other hundreds from inside the city joined the procession. The whole city seemed to be moving with it. Swift runners went by side streets to warn the temple authorities that the young prophet from Galilee was coming with a huge army. Quickly the guards were called out but there was nothing they could do. The crowd was too large for them. An appeal for help was sent to Pilate, the Roman governor. He sent some of his soldiers but they saw that the man leading the procession seemed peaceful. It looked to them like a crowd of pil-

And they came to Jerusalem. And he entered the temple and
began to drive out those who sold and those who bought in the
temple, and he overturned the tables of the money-changers
and the seats of those who sold pigeons. (Mark 11:15.)

grims going up to the temple to worship and they did not try to stop them.

At the gate of the temple, Jesus dismounted from the donkey and entered on foot, the crowd swarming behind him. In the Court of the Gentiles were the booths just as they had been when he was a boy, and the keepers of the booths continued to try to outshout each other as they sold their goods. Here were the moneychangers making their high profits off the poor. Just beyond them were those who sold the doves with their trained birds. As he watched, a dove was being released by a woman. It flew straight toward the wall.

Suddenly fierce anger burned in him, and Jesus walked toward the nearest moneychanger's table. The moneychanger saw a large, strong, angry man coming toward him and, grabbing up the coins he could, he fled from the table. The strong hands of Jesus reached out, seized the heavy table and flung it with a crash against the wall, sending coins flying everywhere.

When the last moneychanger and merchant had fled from the temple area, the crowds became silent and Jesus spoke to them in a quiet but clear voice:

"Is it not written, 'My house shall be called
a house of prayer for all the nations'? But you
have made it a den of robbers."

—Mark 11:17

For more than an hour Jesus taught the crowd as they listened in awe to him, forgetting that it was long past their lunch time. Again and again he explained to them that the kingdom of God was a spiritual kingdom and not one of force and bloodshed.

After his talk he led the men of the crowd into the inner court of the temple. It was so quiet they could

111

hear the choirs chanting as they entered. Nothing had been disturbed here and the priests were going about their work as if nothing had happened.

Caiaphas (kā'e-fas), the high priest that year, knew what Jesus had done and was greatly displeased. By driving out the moneychangers Jesus had discredited the way he conducted the temple and interfered with one of the chief sources of income for the temple.

The high priest was appointed by the Roman governor. In order to be appointed a man had to be in favor with the Romans and able to keep his fellow-Jews peaceful. The Romans tolerated no disturbances among the people they ruled. Therefore, Caiaphas could not allow this prophet from Galilee to come in and upset the running of the temple. He called members of the Council to discuss the situation.

Some of the Council were in a rage over what Jesus had done and wanted to arrest him immediately. Calmer members pointed out that they would not dare do this. If they should arrest Jesus in front of the crowd gathered about him, they would come to his defense and soon a riot would be started. Others thought it would be enough to warn Jesus and send him and his disciples back to Galilee. Then Caiaphas expressed his judgment:

> "You know nothing at all; you do not understand that it is expedient for you that one man should die for the people, and that the whole nation should not perish."
>
> —John 11:49-50

Most of the Council agreed with the high priest that Jesus should be put to death. Nicodemus, a member of the Council and one who had been interested in Jesus' teaching, reminded the high priest that the Jewish law provided that no man could be condemned without a hearing.

Caiaphas stared at Nicodemus a minute, then, with his voice shaking with anger, he shouted, "Are you a Galilean? Are you a follower of this Jesus?" He knew that Nicodemus was right. Jewish law demanded that no one be condemned to death until he had been given a fair trial. Nicodemus turned his head aside under the stern gaze of Caiaphas. He said nothing.

Throwing caution to the wind, the high priest ordered the temple police to arrest Jesus at once. But the police were not in accord with the high priest, for they made only a halfhearted attempt to follow Jesus out of the city and find his camp.

When Jesus returned boldly to the temple the next day, the temple police kept a close watch on him but did not try to arrest him. They listened, as did the crowds, to the wise teachings of this bold Galilean and their hearts were warmed by his stories about the love of a Father God. How could they arrest a man who was doing nothing but good?

Meanwhile Jesus had finished a day of teaching in the temple and, as he was leaving, he passed by the offering chest. A rich Pharisee had just dropped his offering into the chest. He let each coin drop singly so people could count them and see how large an amount he had given. When he had finished his show, a poorly dressed widow slipped up to the chest and dropped two small coins quietly, then moved away, but not before Jesus had taken note of what she had done. Calling his disciples to him, he said:

"Truly, I say to you, this poor widow has put in more than all those who are contributing to the treasury. For they all contributed out of

113

their abundance; but she out of her poverty has put in everything she had, her whole living."

—Mark 12:43-44

On Tuesday, Jesus did not appear in the temple and the high priest feared that he had slipped away to Galilee where he would have no authority over him. But about noon something happened that made Caiaphas feel much better. A messenger came saying that Judas, one of Jesus' disciples, had come to the temple and wanted to see him. The high priest lost no time sending for Judas, but it took a long time to find out what he wanted. When he finally discovered it, he nearly shouted for joy. This disciple of Jesus was willing to tell where Jesus might be found alone at night. The high priest agreed to pay him for the information.

That night, Jesus went to the house of Mary and Martha at Bethany. There a woman brought an alabaster jar of costly perfume and anointed his head. Judas, watching, began to feel uneasy over his dealings with the high priest. To cover up his own guilt he tried to find something wrong in someone else. He muttered that it would be better for this woman to have sold the ointment and given the money to the poor than to waste it by pouring it on Jesus' head.

Jesus saw the look upon Judas' face and knew the dark thoughts in his heart.

With one of his own disciples ready to turn against him, Jesus knew that the hour he had dreaded was at hand and he must make final preparations for it. Early on Thursday morning he sent some of his trusted disciples into the city to prepare a place where they would eat together the ancient Passover supper. The place must be kept secret, so he gave some strange directions as to how they were to find it.

And he sent two of his disciples, and said to them, "Go into the city, and a man carrying a jaw of water will meet you; follow him, and wherever he enters, say to the householder, ' Teacher says, Where is my guest room, whe am to eat the passover with my disciples?" ⌐ he will show you a large upper room furnished and ready; there prepare for us." And the disciples set out and went to the city, and found it as he had told them; and they prepared the passover. —Mark 14:13-16

During the day the old quarrel about who was most important among the Twelve broke out again. It was touched off by James and John. Coming up to Jesus they asked that Jesus give them the highest positions in his new kingdom.

Jesus realized that they misunderstood his teaching and the kind of kingdom he was setting up. After a pause he turned to the two sons and asked, "Are you willing to endure what I shall have to endure? It is not going to be easy. Do you still want the highest positions?"

James and John answered, "Yes, we will do whatever is required." But they did not realize what a great promise they had given, for they did not understand as yet that Jesus meant his death. Later they did know and they kept their promise bravely, James being the first of the Twelve to die for his faith.

When the other disciples heard about the matter, they were angry at James and John for trying to get ahead of them. Jesus was aware of the jealousy among the disciples so he called them all together. Once again he explained that his kingdom was not like the kingdoms of earth and that there would be no places of authority in it. No one was to lord it over anyone else but each was to become great through service.

115

". . . I then, your Lord and Teacher, have washed your feet.
. . . Truly, truly, I say to you, a servant is not greater than his
master." (John 13:14, 16.)

"You know that those who are supposed to rule over the Gentiles lord it over them, and their great men exercise authority over them. But it shall not be so among you; but whoever would be great among you must be your servant, and whoever would be first among you must be slave of all."
—Mark 10:42*b*-44

In spite of what Jesus had said the disciples remained in a bad humor with one another throughout the day. As they arrived at the house where they were to eat the Passover supper, several of them would not speak to James and John, and no one wanted to be "slave of all" as Jesus had taught.

Now it was the custom in those days to greet dinner guests at the door, remove their sandals and wash their feet before they went barefooted to the table. One of the disciples should have considered it his honored privilege to render this service but, being in a bad humor, no one would do it. Each kicked off his sandals at the door and went to the table with his feet unwashed. A few minutes later, Jesus removed his outer robe, tied a large towel around himself, took up a bowl of water, and began washing their feet.

Peter realized at once how wrong they had been and the thought caused him to feel ashamed. When Jesus came to him, he cried out in protest, "I can't have you wash my feet!"

"Peter, I must. You will never understand me if you do not let me wash your feet," Jesus replied gently.

Strong, but tender-hearted Peter was quick to change once he saw he was wrong. "Lord, not only my feet, wash my hands and my head."

Jesus only smiled at him and said that was not necessary. Then he went on around the table washing the feet of the other disciples.

The meal consisted of a lamb, roasted whole, and some

"Take, eat; this is my body." And he took a cup . . . saying,
"Drink of it, all of you; for this is my blood of the covenant,
which is poured out for many for the forgiveness of sins."
(Matthew 26:26-28.)

dry bread dipped in bitter herbs mixed with water. The menu was exactly the same as it had been for hundreds of years and was just like the one Jesus had eaten with his parents 20 years before in this same city.

During the meal Jesus became very sad and he could not keep the tears from his eyes. More than once he looked at Judas, but Judas kept looking down at the table and would not lift his eyes to his Teacher. Jesus wanted so much to reach him, to turn him back from the thing he was about to do. Perhaps if he let Judas know that he knew about the 30 pieces of silver, it would make a difference.

Looking at Judas, but speaking to the group, Jesus said, "One of you will betray me."

The room became very still. Could it be possible that one of the disciples would turn Jesus over to the police? Ever since the cleansing of the temple, the Twelve had been dodging the temple officers. It had become almost a game with them and each disciple had kept watch lest the police come upon their Master when there was no one around to protect him. Would one of their own group now turn traitor and help the police arrest Jesus?

Peter, as usual, was the first to speak. In a hoarse whisper he said, "Is it I?" He waited, afraid of the answer he might receive. He, who had failed so often, could he betray his Master?

Slowly Jesus shook his head and a great wave of relief swept over Peter. It was not he who would do this awful thing. John and James were next, each asking, "Is it I?" They had been the cause of the quarrel that day among the disciples and they still felt guilty over it. Again there was the slow shake of the head and the wave of relief. Neither of them would do this awful thing. The other disciples now asked Jesus, all the same question, "Is it I?" All, that is, except Judas, who said not a word.

When Judas' silence had become noticeable he finally

said, to cover up, "Is it I?" But Jesus knew it was too late to reach him. He could not hear the love and longing in Jesus' voice. He was like one possessed. It seemed almost that he could not help himself now and was being driven by some dark power to betray his best friend for 30 pieces of silver.

When Jesus saw it was no use, he whispered to Judas, "What you are going to do, do quickly." Judas left at once. It was terrible to think that one of his own disciples would be the cause of his death.

Jesus knew now that his death was coming very soon but he had one last thing he must do. Taking bread, he gave thanks, then gave each disciple a small piece. Jesus explained, "Take this and eat it for it represents my body." Then he took a cup and gave thanks for it and passed it to the disciples, saying, "Each of you drink of this, for it represents my blood."

Slowly the cup went around the circle of disciples and each took a sip of it though none fully understood the meaning of this act. Later they would know and would repeat this part of their last supper together at every evening meal. Later the church would take this simple ceremony and make of it a beautiful act of worship known as communion.

Then Jesus with the eleven disciples, Judas having left earlier to carry out his bargain with the high priest, sang a hymn and went out to the Mount of Olives.

Palm Branches, Coins and Cup of Death

The symbol of the palm branches, the coins, and the cup of death at the beginning of this chapter illustrates three events in the last week of Jesus' life. The palm branches represent the triumphal entry of Jesus into Jerusalem. The coins of silver represent the money paid to Judas to betray Jesus, and the cup represents the death of Jesus.

120

10.

When Everything Goes Wrong

As JESUS AND THE ELEVEN disciples walked
slowly toward the olive grove, he talked earnestly. Difficult as this night was going to be
for him, it would be more difficult for them. He
sought to give them comfort and courage:

"Let not your hearts be troubled; believe in
God, believe also in me. In my Father's house
are many rooms; if it were not so, would I have
told you that I go to prepare a place for you?"
—John 14:1-2

Thomas, like the other disciples, could not
understand what he was talking about. More

than once Jesus had spoken of his death and going away, but Thomas just could not believe it. "Master, we do not know where you are going," he cried.

> Jesus said to him, "I am the way, and the truth, and the life; no one comes to the Father, but by me."
>
> —John 14:6

Jesus' words were a strange, strange answer to Thomas. Later he was to understand them, but tonight he did not know what Jesus meant.

Then Jesus began to warn them that they would do things before the night was over that would make them deeply ashamed of themselves. Their faith in him would be tested. Each would be forced to decide to stand by him or turn from him.

This was more than Peter could bear. Quickly he spoke up, "Master, even though all the others fail you, I will not. Never."

Jesus gently laid his hand on the shoulder of this rough-and-ready fisherman and said to him, "Peter, this very night before a new day dawns, before the cock crows twice, you will claim that you never even knew me, not only once but three times."

Peter was shocked and cried out, "I will not deny you. Even if I have to die with you, I will not turn against you."

Jesus only patted him on the shoulder and said no more as he continued on toward the olive grove.

Then the soldiers of the governor took Jesus into the prae- ➤ torium . . . And they stripped him and put a scarlet robe upon him and plaiting a crown of thorns they put it on his head . . . and they spat upon him. (Matthew 27:27-31.)

When the little band arrived at the Mount of Olives Jesus moved away from the disciples. Peter, James and John, knowing that he was going to pray, followed along. When Jesus found a quiet place he knelt to pray. Peter, James and John stopped a little distance from him so that they would not intrude on the Master. Jesus prayed so earnestly that drops of sweat formed on his brow which, in the moonlight, looked like great drops of blood. He prayed:

> "My Father, if it be possible, let this cup pass from me; nevertheless, not as I will, but as thou wilt."
>
> —Matthew 26:39

Jesus knew that, even as he was praying, Judas was leading the police to his hiding place and that the "cup" of his death was very near. He was not afraid to die but he wanted to live as long as possible. He had so much to live for. His disciples needed to learn much more about the kingdom. People needed the good news of the gospel preached to them. There was still much to do; it was hard to die and leave it all.

Over and over again he uttered this brief prayer, listening between times for God's answer. Clearly God's answer came back, "No." Strangely, Jesus grew calm when he got this answer. He knew he could trust his heavenly Father. If the answer was no, there was a good reason for it. If he must die, he could trust God to use his death for some great purpose. He had followed God's will all his life and now he was not afraid to follow his Father's will even unto death.

Now that he had his answer for his own life, he began to pray for his disciples. Not only did he pray that his disciples might stay together and work together, he also prayed that all the Christians throughout the ages should also live and work together in love and good will.

When he arose from his prayers, he could see a band of men coming up the road toward the olive grove. He knew his hour had come. Quickly awakening Peter, James and John he returned to the camp and aroused the other disciples. In a few minutes the band turned into the grove with Judas at its head.

Since few of these men knew Jesus, Judas had agreed to identify him. He was to walk right up to Jesus and greet him as a close friend, kissing him on the cheek. At this sign the men were to grab Jesus.

"Hail, Master!" cried Judas. As he kissed him, Jesus said to him, "Judas, would you betray the Son of man with a kiss?"

Judas' heart was touched by these words. The tall figure of the man he had once left everything to follow, the hurt in the voice that cried out to him, made him suddenly aware of the awful thing he had done. He fell back from Jesus as if he had been struck a blow. Shame flooded over him and his face burned as if it were on fire. All at once he wished he had never bargained with the high priest, but it was too late. Already the mob had surrounded Jesus and their rough hands reached out to grab him. Judas hid his face in his hands and fled through the trees.

One or two of the temple officers had come along with Judas' band. These placed Jesus under arrest. Then Peter and the other disciples, who only an hour or so ago had promised that they would never desert him, took to their heels and fled, leaving Jesus alone with his captors. At the very moment when he needed them most, everyone had run away. It must have filled him with despair. Could the kingdom of God be established through weak men like these? Would everything he had worked for disappear? This was a hard moment for Jesus, but he had learned to trust God and he was sure he could trust him even in this.

The mob led Jesus away, first to the high priest's house near the temple. It was after midnight when they arrived. But the high priest opened court at once even though the law required that a prisoner be given at least a full day to get legal help and witnesses before he should be brought to trial. The high priest did not hesitate to break the law, for he knew he dared not keep Jesus in prison. Jesus had so many friends in the city that they could break down the strongest prison there.

Loafers were called in off the streets, given money, and told what to say about Jesus. But many of these were so ignorant they got their stories mixed up and the trial was about to break up with no charge against Jesus.

Then the high priest asked Jesus point blank, "Are you the Christ?"

What should Jesus say? There were some in the courtroom who believed in him. If he refused to answer, would he weaken their faith? If he answered boldly, would the priests have him stoned to death on the spot? Jewish law made it a death penalty for anyone to claim he was God or equal to God. As the Son of God, Jesus would be claiming to be equal to God.

He hesitated a moment and took the brave way. "I am," he answered.

The high priest was delighted but he pretended to look shocked. He tore his clothes, moaned, and tried to cry. Then he shouted in triumph, "He has made himself equal to God, what do we need with more witnesses? He is worthy of death!"

Quickly the judges voted the death penalty and would have taken Jesus and killed him at once except for the fact that the Roman government did not allow the Jewish court to put anyone to death without the governor's consent. The chief priest took Jesus to Pilate, the agent of the Roman government. Pilate talked to Jesus and could find no crime that he had committed. But the crowd would not accept this and when Pilate heard from them that Jesus was a Galilean and belonged in Herod's province, he sent him over to the court of Herod, the Jewish governor of Galilee, who was visiting in Jerusalem.

Meanwhile some of the disciples had got up a little courage and had followed the mob to the high priest's house, but they did not try to go in. Peter stood out in the yard warming his hands at a fire. A young girl noticed the queer look on Peter's face and she thought she could have some fun teasing him. "You are one of the followers of Jesus," she said.

Fear seized Peter and he looked about for a place to run but there were people everywhere. "I do not know what you mean," he stammered. Then he got away from the fire quickly. But at the gate the girl found him and again said he was one of Jesus' band. This time Peter openly denied that he had ever known Jesus and the girl left him.

A few minutes later someone else asked the same question and Peter began to swear as he had in his old fisherman days and cried, "I do not know this man of whom you speak."

In the silence that followed Peter's outburst a rooster crowed for the dawn. A moment later Jesus was led out of the high priest's house. As he passed by Peter, their eyes met. In that moment Peter remembered the words of the Lord that before the cock crowed he would deny Jesus three times. Peter was overcome with shame. He left the courtyard hurriedly and wept bitterly as soon as he was alone. He, who had bragged that he would die with his Lord if necessary, had denied him before a harmless young girl. Could he ever be forgiven of his faithlessness and cowardice? Peter did not know and it made him weep the more bitterly.

Jesus was taken to the court of Herod. This was the same Herod who had killed John the Baptist. Jesus refused to speak to him or answer a single question he asked. So the evil-minded ruler turned Jesus over to some of his soldiers for punishment. Since they had heard that he was thought of as a king and a prophet, they put a royal robe on him and a crown on his head, but the crown was made of thorns that dug deeply into his brow, causing blood to trickle down his face. Then they blindfolded him, and after spitting in his face, kicking and slapping him, they demanded that he "prophesy" which struck him. But he spoke not a word. Nothing the soldiers could do to him would cause him to cry out in anger or pain. The rough soldiers wondered at his self-control and soon tired of mistreating him.

At daylight on Friday the high priest hurried to the office of the Roman governor. Pilate did not like to be waked up so early in the morning but he listened to the high priest's story of how he had caught a very dangerous man who had set himself up as a king against Roman rule. He did not mention the fact that the Jewish court had tried him on an altogether different charge, that of making himself equal to God. The high priest was sly enough to know Pilate would not be interested in such a charge.

Pilate reluctantly consented to look into the case. He listened to the enemies of Jesus hurling their charges against him. He was amazed at the calmness of Jesus who stood in quiet dignity refusing to answer the wild charges brought against him.

Pilate took Jesus aside to see if he could find what was at the bottom of this trouble. When they were alone he asked, "These men charge that you have set yourself up as a king. Are you really a king?"

For the second time since his trial began, Jesus spoke, "My kingship is not of this world."

It did not take Pilate long to see that this whole matter was due to the spite and anger of the high priests. Although he did not want to be responsible for the death of an innocent man, he had to keep the good will of the chief priests. Suddenly it came to him; there was a way out.

> Now at the feast the governor was accustomed to release for the crowd any one prisoner whom they wanted. And they had then a notorious prisoner, called Barabbas. So when they had gathered, Pilate said to them, "Whom do you want me to release for you, Barabbas or Jesus who is called Christ?" . . . Now the chief priests and the elders persuaded the people to ask for Barabbas and destroy Jesus. The governor again said to them, "Which of the two do you want me to release for you?" And they said, "Barabbas." Pilate said to them, "Then what shall I do with Jesus who is called Christ?" They all said, "Let him be crucified."
>
> So when Pilate saw that he was gaining nothing, but rather that a riot was beginning he took water and washed his hands before the crowd, saying, "I am innocent of this man's blood; see to it yourselves."
>
> —Matthew 27:15-17, 20-22, 24

Someone shouted, "Crucify him!" Persons who had been prompted by the high priest took up the cry: "Crucify him!" Many others in the curious crowd were caught up in the excitement and joined in shouting, "Crucify him! Crucify him!"

Now Pilate was a cowardly man and when he heard the cry of the crowd he was afraid he was going to have

129

a riot on his hands. "Better to punish one innocent man than have trouble," he thought. So he released Barabbas, and sentenced Jesus to be whipped. Perhaps this would satisfy the mob.

Thirty and nine times the strong arm of the Roman soldier rose and fell. Each time it laid across the bare back of Jesus the sting of a leather whip. Thirty and nine times Jesus' body trembled beneath the lash. Stroke by stroke his back was cut to ribbons until there was not a whole piece of skin on it. Blood stained his clothes and the whip. But he stood calmly through it all. Only once did his lips move and a soldier ran up to see if he had some confession to make, but all he could hear was, "Father, forgive them."

After this, Jesus was brought before the crowd again. He was still stripped to the waist and Pilate had him turn around so everyone could see how terribly he had been beaten. It was enough to turn the heart of anyone. Pilate in pity cried out, "Here is the man!" But there was no pity in the hearts of Jesus' enemies. At the high priest's signal they began once more crying, "Crucify him! Crucify him!" Finally Pilate gave in and ordered Jesus crucified. He thought it the easiest way out.

But standing in the crowd was one man who did not shout, "Crucify him." Instead he seemed to try to hide each time he heard the awful cry and when Pilate finally gave the order for crucifixion, a look of horror spread over his face. This man was Judas and he still carried with him those 30 pieces of silver he had been fool enough to take.

And when they had crucified him, they divided his garments➤ among them by casting lots. . . . And over his head they put the charge against him, which read, "This is Jesus, the King of the Jews." (Matthew 27:35, 37.)

"They are going to crucify him," he sobbed. "O my Master, what awful thing have I done to you?" But there was now no one to hear his cry for they were leading Jesus away to prepare him for death by the cruelest method known to man.

Crucifixion was a grim business but the Roman soldiers were used to it. It was just part of the day's work to them and it did not take them long to get ready. Two bandits had already been condemned to be crucified on this day and their crosses were ready and lying in the courtyard. To add a third cross was not much more work. Within an hour they were ready and they formed a little procession as a company of a hundred soldiers marched out of the governor's palace with the three prisoners in their midst.

So swiftly had the high priest and the other enemies of Jesus done their work, that the friends of Jesus did not know what had happened to him until they saw him as a prisoner of the Roman soldiers. They were shocked but they did not know what to do and they had no leader to show them. "Where is Peter?" they asked, thinking he could tell them what course of action they should take. But Peter was still hiding, ashamed to show his face after denying his Lord in the night.

"Where is Judas?" others asked, remembering how he had once helped organize them into an army. With such an army they could rescue Jesus from this small company of Roman soldiers.

Where was Judas? No one had seen him in the last hour but if they had known where to look, they could have seen his lifeless body swinging at the end of a rope from a tree just outside the city. Poor Judas! All his life he had loved only himself. Once he had thought he loved Jesus and had followed him, but soon he was thinking how important he had become to Jesus. He dreamed of the day when Jesus would set up an earthly kingdom. He would have a high office in that kingdom and everyone would have to look up to him. When that dream failed because Jesus had refused to become such a king, he had turned against Jesus. He had lived in his dreams with a Judas who always was going to become great and famous. Now he had to face himself as a traitor and he could not stand it. He had loved only Judas and Judas had failed him.

Where was Judas? If they had looked just down the path on the other side of the gate, they could have seen him still swaying.

With the leaders gone there was nothing the people could do for their friend. On, on went the procession of anguish and tears. The heavy cross cut deeper and deeper into Jesus' back, bruised and bleeding from the whipping he had received. His body trembled with pain and fatigue but step by step he moved along, determined to go as far as he could. Just outside the city gate he fell in a faint. His strong body had obeyed his stronger will just as long as it could, but it could go no further. Quickly the Roman soldiers surrounded him, helping him up. He must not be allowed to die until they could get a chance to crucify him. They examined his back and even they, hardened as they were, were shocked by his condition.

A man by the name of Simon of the country of Cyrene was standing nearby, and the captain of the guard ordered him to carry the cross for Jesus. It is said that this man later became a Christian and was greatly honored by the church as the man who carried the cross.

Now the procession moved outside the city to a dirty, little hill called Golgotha, or Calvary. The crosses were laid on the ground and holes dug at the end of each. The prisoners were stripped of almost all of their clothing and made to lie down on the crosses with their arms outstretched.

They had been offered some drugged potion to deaden

133

the pain of this terrible moment, but Jesus refused to drink any. The two bandits were nailed to their crosses first, screaming and cursing and held down by a dozen strong soldiers.

Now the executioner came to Jesus who was lying quietly on his cross. This was the darkest moment in the history of the world, a moment when it must have been hard for God to keep on loving the world. A large, rough nail was placed upright in the palm of Jesus' hand. Then the executioner struck a swift, hard blow and the nail was driven all the way through that hand and into the wood. As swiftly another nail went through the other hand. Jesus flinched but he did not cry out. Then came the supreme moment of suffering; the bare feet were laid one on top of the other. A very large nail was necessary this time for it must go through both feet and into the wood. With all his might the executioner swung and the great nail ripped through flesh, bones, nerves, and muscles in a blinding, searing flash of pain.

Now the crosses were raised and the earth shuddered as they were dropped in the holes. The whole weight of the bodies now hung upon those awful nails. The prisoner was in so much pain he could not be still and yet if he moved, he only tore the flesh around the nails. This might go on for hours, for the worst thing about crucifixion was that death was very slow in coming. Reports are that men have lived and suffered for as long as three days before death came to release them.

Up to now no word had escaped Jesus' lips. He had borne his pain in the strong faith that God would see him through this awful agony and he knew that as long as God was with him he could bear it. With the fierce rush of pain after the cross was lifted up, he did cry out but his cry was a prayer, "Father, forgive them. They do not know what they do."

By now a large crowd had gathered to watch the

crucifixion. The enemies of Jesus were there to rejoice in his suffering and death. The morbid were there, for they seemed to get pleasure out of some other person's misfortune. A few of the friends of Jesus were there, for they had not all deserted him.

Several faithful women wept near his cross. With them was Jesus' mother and by her side stood John, the disciple. Jesus, seeing the two, called out to them in words they would understand but which meant nothing to the curious crowd. "Woman, behold your son!" he said to his mother. Then to John he said, "Behold your mother!" John understood what he meant and from that day cared for Mary as if she were his own mother.

From about nine o'clock in the morning until three in the afternoon Jesus endured the agony of slow death by crucifixion. His body became infected from the nail wounds. His forehead burned with fever and his lips were parched with thirst. But he bore his suffering with dignity, calmly waiting for the release of death which came sooner than was expected. It was as if God could not stand to see his Son suffer any longer and after six hours brought the horrible torture to a swift end.

At three o'clock Jesus cried with a loud voice, "Father, into thy hands I commit my spirit!" His body went limp on the cross and his suffering was over. The high priest smiled happily when word was brought that Jesus was dead. He had destroyed this bold prophet from Galilee and never again would he stir up the people. He thought he was through with this Jesus forever.

Now Joseph of Arimathea did a strange and courageous thing. He was a rich Pharisee and a member of the Jewish court, but he was friendly toward Jesus. He had not had the courage to follow Jesus while he lived but, now that he was dead, he bravely revealed his friendliness toward him.

135

The high priest had used his money and power to destroy Jesus. Joseph resolved to use his to give Jesus a decent burial. It was the custom of the Roman government to throw out the bodies of persons crucified to be eaten by wild animals. Joseph could not bear to think of that happening, so he went to Pilate and asked for the body of Jesus. Pilate could not refuse so wealthy and powerful a man and granted his request.

But Joseph had to hurry; he had but an hour or so to get Jesus down from the cross and bury him before the sabbath began at six o'clock. Fortunately, Joseph had a tomb in a garden not too far away. Here he and his helpers carried the body of Jesus. There was no time to put spices about the body. They could only wrap it in a clean grave cloth and lay it in the tomb, a cavelike place dug out of a rocky hillside at the edge of Joseph's garden. It was the place where he himself had expected to be buried some day but he gladly gave up the place for the body of his friend.

There was just time to lay the body inside and roll a huge, round stone over the opening before the horns began to blow in Jerusalem announcing that the sabbath had begun.

The Cross

The symbol at the beginning of this chapter represents the crucifixion of Jesus. The Roman cross represents the cross upon which Jesus was hanged. The nails symbolize those which were used to pierce his hands and feet. There are at least two meanings for the circle. In accordance with the cross and nails, it could represent the crown of thorns. In a broader sense, the circle, because it has no beginning or end, could mean the eternal love of God for all men.

136

11.

Sunrise Forever

THAT SABBATH WAS THE saddest the disciples had ever known. Their beloved Teacher had died like a common criminal on a Roman cross. They no longer had a leader and they felt that, without him, all he had taught them about the kingdom of God had no meaning. There seemed now nothing to do but to return to their old jobs and forget they had ever been disciples.

Mary Magdalene and Mary, the mother of James, decided that the least they could do would be to give Jesus' body a better burial than it had received. As soon as the sabbath was over, they bought spices and perfumes to put on his body and planned to go early next morning to the tomb.

No one was ever sure just what happened to these women on that Sunday morning. They were so excited they were never able to tell all the details.

At dawn they had gone slowly and sadly to Joseph's garden to do what they could for Jesus' body. Within an hour they had come running back, out of breath and shouting, "He is not there; he is risen!" One woman would start to tell something of what had happened and the other would break in to tell something else. Then they would fall to crying and laughing at the same time.

Finally the women became calm enough to tell that when they had arrived at the tomb, they found the stone rolled away from the entrance. Looking into the tomb they had seen a strange young man sitting there.

> And he said to them, "Do not be amazed; you seek Jesus of Nazareth, who was crucified. He has risen, he is not here; see the place where they laid him."
>
> —Mark 16:6

It had been too wonderful to believe, and they had looked for a long time at the empty space where Jesus' body had lain. Slowly it had begun to dawn on them. It was true that he had risen from the dead. He was alive again.

Then the young man said to them,

> "But go, tell his disciples and Peter that he is going before you to Galilee; there you will see him, as he told you."
>
> —Mark 16:7

Peter was standing at the edge of the group of disciples when the women brought their news. He was still too ashamed of himself to say much to anyone. He, like the other disciples, could not believe what the women were saying but he was quick to note what the young man had said, "Go, tell his disciples *and Peter.*" Did this mean that the Lord had sent him a message to lift him out of his shame? He must find out. Not waiting to hear more from the women, when they found him, Peter set out for the tomb, with John right at his heels. The two began to run and John, being younger, soon outran Peter.

When they arrived at the tomb they found it empty, just as the women had said, but there was no young man about. After looking around carefully, they returned to the city and began to make preparations to go back to Galilee.

That night as they were having supper, suddenly there was Someone in the room. There could be no question about it; this was Jesus as they had known him and yet so strangely different. At first, they were afraid. Then they heard a voice, and it was the voice they had known and loved so well. "Peace," Jesus said, "peace be with you." After Christ was gone, they all felt a deep joy in their hearts but still they could not believe that he was really alive.

For a period of 40 days the disciples, alone or together, would often feel the Presence of the living Christ near them.

There is no record of just when it happened or how, but sometime during these 40 days the disciples became sure that their beloved Teacher was alive again. At first they simply could not believe it; no one had ever returned from the dead before. But one day they were all sure that he was alive.

On that day their eyes were opened. So many

Peter and John at the empty tomb.

things Jesus had taught which they had not understood at the time, now became plain to them. As the conviction grew that Jesus was alive, they began to meet together again. The faithful women joined the 11 disciples. Other believers joined the group until their number grew to about 120 persons.

We can imagine their conversation as they began to understand that Jesus had truly risen from the dead.

"Do you remember," asked one of the disciples, "the answer he gave the Pharisees when they asked for a sign? He told them no sign would be given them except the sign of Jonah. Now I see what he meant. Jonah was in the fish for three days. Jesus was in the tomb for three days, or parts of three days, then he came back to life. Truly, he knew what he was talking about."

"I remember, too," said Thomas, "how he told me once that he was the way and the truth and the life. I thought it strange then but I see it now. We are to follow him. He is the way for us. He is the truth about God. He is the life we are to live."

John spoke up, "I see why he would not let us make our kind of king out of him and set up the kind of kingdom we wanted. His kingdom is so much greater than the one we had in mind. His is a kingdom of love and good will that takes in the whole world. He is the king, not just of us Jews but of the whole world, for he is God's own Son."

James broke in, "I thought once he should save the world by raising an army and defeating the Romans. Now I see that we are to be soldiers of peace and spread the good news of his life and teachings everywhere. We will conquer Rome, not with a sword but by love and service."

"Do you suppose he would have forgiven Judas?" one of the others asked.

141

Thomas thought a long time about this. "Yes, I think he would. You remember Jesus asked forgiveness for the men who nailed him to the cross!"

Nicodemus, the Pharisee, who had recently joined the group of believers spoke up next. "Through his death on the cross, I am beginning to see that Jesus has shown us how much God loves us and how far he is willing to go to save us. I am an old man and have not many years to live but now I am no longer afraid of death. Christ has died and come back from death. He has defeated death, both for himself and for all who believe in and follow him. He is alive forever more, and we, too, shall live!"

On another occasion Peter was talking about his new understanding of the kingdom of God. "Now we can understand," he said, "just what kind of king our Lord is. How slow we were to see it! How much we must have tried his love! He has become the King of kings and the Lord of lords. Sin and evil tried to destroy him but could not for he is stronger than all the forces of evil put together. Even death could not defeat him and it cannot defeat his kingdom. He will reign always, and his kingdom shall never end."

Later, the group of 120 gathered at the old campsite on the Mount of Olives and Peter spoke to them. As he closed, there was a stir among the trees. Suddenly the living Christ was with them once more. Somehow they understood that this would be the last experience like this. Hereafter Christ would come to them as spirit and would speak only to the inner heart of each. He would never be far away.

It was a glorified Christ who spoke to them now, one who was truly the Prince of heaven, the Son of God. A brilliant light seemed to flood the sky as Christ spoke.

142

And Jesus came and said to them, "All authority in heaven and on earth has been given to me. Go therefore and make disciples of all nations, baptizing them in the name of the Father and of the Son and of the Holy Spirit, teaching them to observe all that I have commanded you; and lo, I am with you always, to the close of the age."

—Matthew 28:18-20

Slowly the light faded and he disappeared. But there was no sadness in the hearts of the disciples. Their Lord had given them a great task—they were to tell all the world about the kingdom of love. Also he had promised to be with them always. Wherever they went, he would be there ahead of them. Whatever they did, he would be there helping them. Whatever the danger, he would be there to share with them and give them victory, even over death.

The light of God's truth had broken upon the world. Never again would men live in the darkness of ignorance about God. The sunrise had come on forever.

Now Jesus did many other signs in the presence of the disciples, which are not written in this book; but these are written that you may believe that Jesus is the Christ, the Son of God, and that believing you may have life in his name.

—John 20:30-31

The Roman Cross

The cross at the beginning of this chapter is one of the most common Christian symbols. Protestant churches choose to use the *empty* cross as a symbol of his having risen from the dead.

143